LIMBO

A
NOVEL **Joel Hammil**
BY

LIMBO

ARBOR HOUSE New York

C, 2

TO NADIA, AN AUTISTIC CHILD,
SOMEWHERE.

A nobel laureate whose pioneering mind
research has separated him from his
most cherished ethics experiments with
an incongruously brilliant prostitute
in a top-secret project with implications both inspiring and frightening.

CHAPTER ONE

THE BISTRO in the East Fifties just off Lexington was
what is known as discreet. The cuisine, under the direction of a protégé of the great Henri Soulé, was faultless,
the service and ambience no less so; and above all, the
well-heeled, as one had to be, could dine here with someone they would be uneasy with at "21" or some such oasis.

Rafaele, the captain, stood correctly, pencil poised, as
he jotted down the choices of the party of four. The
matter of the wine was being ritualized by Marty Wallin
who smiled deferentially across the linened table.

"The Gewürztztraminer '68 okay, Dana?" he asked.

Dana Bettinger, a corporate tax attorney with several
Saudis rumored to be among his clients, murmured a
"fine." Why put Marty down by saying a Seven-Up
would suit him as well? A Perrier, to be fancier.

Who cares? he thought. If Marty wants his little game
before the dolls, let him have it. It'll cost him the tab. He
also knew Marty Wallin could afford it. He was into

precious metals these days; besides, the word had it that when Washington or Big Mac tightened the budget screws a bit, Marty Wallin was usually in on the scotch-taping.

The captain directed his oiliest smile toward Connie Keenan. It was owner's policy. The "girls" were always to be given special handling, since by wrinkling a nose when their johns suggested a bite there, they had it in their power to wreck a joint.

"Mademoiselle has selected her other vegetable with the *gigot?*" he asked in that way that could make a hooker forget who she was.

Connie had indeed selected her other vegetable, but the immediate problem was she couldn't say it, leaving her confused and troubled. Not that it mattered one way or another whether she got mushrooms or lima beans. Whatever. It was the frustration. To have in mind asparagus, visualize the damned things. Taste them with their Hollandaise, as she preferred it. She even knew her pee would smell for a day. And yet the word eluded her; and the frustration was compounded by the fact that more and more frequently it was happening with other words as well.

"Whatever you think, Rafaele," she said casually as possible.

"Perhaps the *choux de Bruxelles aux Marrons?*" was suggested and agreed to.

The apparent ordinary exchange was hardly noticed by two men into their usual money talk. It presently had to do with some Long Island ocean footage. Sylvia, Dana Bettinger's date, was studying her friend Connie, sensing something distinctly amiss.

Across the table she saw a stunning young woman whose coppery hair, Suga-cut, was set off by an emerald-green Halston which did the right things for the tallish figure. The casual onlooker might have thought of her as cool, even remote. This, however, was a reflection of her distress, the almost translucent complexion paler than usual and the classic, well-defined jawline more set. Pronounced.

Any wonder, her friend Sylvia speculated, Connie gets the crème of the johns. The town's shakers and movers.

There was more to Connie Keenan than the obvious. What really set her apart was her special knack for gratifying them with more than sex. To come away feeling a super-lover—a Burt Reynolds—was fine. But puffing up the ego as a man of unusual charm, wit and flair—that was what made her more than worth the price.

Connie's exasperation and distress, tinged with concern, receded. Herself again, she tuned back into the conversation of the two men, a small, admiring smile about her lips as if she knew what it was all about.

"A little encouragement in the right places," Marty Wallin was saying. "Y'know what I mean, and the zoning restrictions disappear." He went on to envision a blueprint of subdivisions with shops, motels, marinas. Millions in profits seemed to sprout with his enthusiasm.

"You great, wonderful man!" Connie's admiring expression said distinctly, belying her thoughts. What a farce! A few hours ago this same pudgy custard in the Ralph Lauren had played out a variation of his fantasy script. Her props included the sensible clothes of a schoolmarm with blouse, heavy skirt and shoes she could only find in a St. Malachy's thrift shop. She had even worn heavy tortoise-shell frames from which she had removed the lenses for fear of an accident in the anticipated tussle.

Harry had stepped outside into the corridor of the chic Third Avenue apartment house to ring the doorbell. Announcing himself as the piano-tuner—they both knew she owned no piano—she unlocked the several

3

bolts and admitted him. Once inside, he produced a realistic toy pistol, then forced her into the bedroom. Connie had pleaded for mercy. She had been made to undress, slowly. He then snatched off her glasses, ripped off her bra. Cowering, she covered her breasts, was ordered to take off her panties. When she could see the bulge in his trousers had reached the proper size, she complied. Upon seeing the source of the bulge exposed, she made a show of awe and terror. Pushed back upon the bed, she fought with just enough strength not to dislodge him. Her fear gradually changed over to a show of "pleasure" —as required by the scenario. Her ecstasy mounted. She thrashed about in its transports. And so forth, until, finally, a few pathetic damp spasms and it was over . . .

"I'm working on what's-his-name over at the teachers' union in behalf of you-know-who," Marty was saying. His nail-polished fingers twirled a long-stemmed wine glass which glistened like a jewel. "The sonofabitch has got to feel the city's fate and fiscal integrity is in his hands. Power. You got to affirm their power."

Connie could handle this irony. The contrast between the bullshit and the reality. It wasn't remarkable to her any more. Or unusual. Bizarre needs and quirky hang-ups among the most widely respected citizens. Normal? Abnormalcy became the norm as one ascended the city's social hierarchy. Yet these men at least could afford to reenact their daydreams. She considered the subways— the night streets—the lurkers who couldn't pay—and shuddered. The Marty Wallins could at least expose their secrets, aware it was in a contrived, manufactured setting. She was one of the paid players who performed in their clients' theater of illusions. And yet when it was over, the secret exposed, the post-coitum triste, how often had she seen the powdered-over bruises of the other girls, the pan-makeupped blackened eyes. She her-

4

self had had her own share, and understood it was part and parcel of her *own* script, her own needs—her mordant secret . . .

The brussels sprouts with chestnuts tasted dreadful, she thought. Not that they actually were, but they somehow symbolized the nagging problem of the disremembered asparagus and other words. . . .

She sat in the consultation room of her internist's ground-floor office. Beyond him, through angled blinds, sliced sections of the Park Avenue traffic sped by. A short while ago, in the examining room, the thick, stubby fingers of the middle-aged Viennese had moved deftly in a series of neurological reflex tests, some of which—like the knee-rapping and the following of his forefinger with her eyes—seemed absolutely silly.

"The condition is called aphasia, my dear," he was now saying, "and the cause of it . . ."

She didn't hear anything else. She wasn't listening.

Aphasia! A nice word, she was thinking. It evoked in her the pleasant image of a fuzzy TV commercial with a bouncy-titted beauty in organdy, racing barelegged across a meadow, a handsome young stud in pursuit. Going down in the yielding wildflowers, an oily voice—something like Rafaele's—would come up behind . . . "Spray with Aphasia. Be fresh and fragrant all over—"

But now—intruding—the accented voice was saying something about tumors. Brain tumors.

Brain tumor! Hey, hold on there! she thought. Take it easy! Slow down!

"Probably we'll find it benign. A cyst. A nodule." he was saying. "Still, it puts pressure on a nerve."

We'll find it! she was thinking. That's what he said! We'll find it! Like that! The implication of the simple words took effect—like a dentist's needle, leaving her numb all over. What was this almost cliché comic fellow talking about? This is *me*. These thing happen to others.

5

The specter of her own death loitered beyond the words. The doctor was continuing with "benign," "cyst," but she knew the words for what they were. Dangled hopes, patently false. Who is he kidding?

". . . and of course there must be more testing," he was now saying.

"Naturally," she murmured, her head nodding slowly like a stuffed animal at an auto's rear window.

A day later, the thick glass doors to the lobby of her apartment house swung open. The doorman sprang forward with a "Taxi, miss?" As he went off tooting his whistle for a cab, she put down her small Vuitton bag and peered about.

Couldn't it at least be raining? she thought gloomily.

It was indeed one of those all too rare bright mornings when the city looked—even smelled—good. The outdoor café awnings seemed brighter, more colorful than ever before as aproned men were hosing down the pavements. Not a morning person, it was something of a new experience for her to see the city fresh—not yet spent. Since her visit to Dr. Ephraim, she had fallen into gloomy speculations. She was now thinking, not that the city or the world should be holding their breaths till her crisis was over, but someone should at least be caring. Be concerned. Even the cabbie, when she mentioned the name of the uptown hospital, didn't hide his disappointment it wasn't a trip to Kennedy International.

"Testing," that innocuous word, began innocently enough. Compliance and cooperation gradually changed to jaw-clenching tolerance as she was passed from one group of technicians to another either for a CAT scan, an angiogram, an exploration by sound waves or X rays. Despite the fact she had necessarily made a fine art of separating what was inflicted upon her body from a spe-

6

cial, private part of herself, she felt a buildup of resentment at the hospital staff's cold hands and colder feelings.

"Hold *still*, honey." Click, click. "There, okay, you can *breathe* now." The *chutzpa* of it, Connie thought. I've permission to breathe. She just shot me with fifty million volts, probably giving me cancer if I don't already have it.

Connie, called "ambulatory," didn't have to remain in bed. By the second day of her ordeal she was pacing her room. By now she had become an expert in each single heavy brushstroke of the cheap Van Gogh sunflower print bolted to the wall, and she had long since wearied of the TV's inanities, day and night. She had counted the perforated ceiling squares and the sum invariably came out the same. She had pre-decided it. Even, she'd be okay. Odd—oh, well. There were precisely one hundred and forty-eight squares. She had recounted them a dozen times and felt reassured with each counting. It was almost as if an *I Ching* reading said don't worry.

It was morning now and the weather had changed. Sky and water were one steely gray, the latter running mercurially beneath the nearby bridge. Tugs hurled their bleak calls through the shrouds of morning mists, echoing from the cliffs across the river. Her room was so-called private, and a door opening usually meant another institutional meal or someone after more of one body fluid or another. But now a voice—that familiar, ebullient voice, said, "Goot morning!"

She turned. Doctor Ephraim in his white tunic was accompanied by another similarly clad younger stranger. After the automatic you're-looking-fine, Doctor Ephraim said, "I'd like you to meet Doctor Carlino, one of our finest neurosurgeons."

So! There it is, she thought. The bottom line. Surgeon. Neurosurgeon.

Oddly, she felt nothing. No panic. Nothing, literally. Something akin to a peace came over her. An end was at least in sight. The matter settled. Dr. Ephraim was explaining that the tests showed a small shadow in a region of the brain called the Area of Broca. ". . . at the base of the frontal convolutions of the cerebral cortex. The thing is—and Doctor Carlino agrees—we should have a look at it."

Have a *look* at it, she thought. Let's go down to Gucci's and have a look at some boots . . . Her eyes turned to this new man in her life.

Phillip Carlino was saying evenly, "Whatever it is doesn't belong there."

"A shadow—" she began weakly, seeking solace somewhere.

"Shadows have substance," he interrupted. His olive-pit eyes held hers. He at least wasn't smiling. Thank God for that, at least, she thought.

She hardly heard Doctor Ephraim concurring. Her attention was now fixed upon this new man, her antennae directed toward him. After all, he wasn't just another someone to get it on with. He was the proposed candidate to open her skull and mess about with its contents.

Her first impression wasn't that reassuring, but then she wasn't quite sure what it was supposed to be. She had to line up new guidelines, assess him by unfamiliar criteria. A Marcus Welby he certainly wasn't. No bleeding, tearful heart there. The more she got into her appraisal, the more suspicious she became.

He seemed more like the cabdriver who had brought her to this place. His hands were broad and strong as a stonemason's, the swarthy face bore scars from growing up on the city's streets. His low voice didn't disguise the East Side or South Bronx accent; and yet she was aware had it suggested some Ivy League institution, she would have been even more ill at ease, distrustful. She knew he was there with Doctor Ephraim's approval, and this was somewhat reassuring. She recognized that her doubts—the negative things she saw in him—had their roots in the simple question: Who, after all, is good enough to open her head and poke about? A bit of irony struck her. She had spent years and a small fortune in a wide range of therapies and self-realization modalities, from est to primal, seeking answers to her self-destructiveness, and now she was definitely experiencing a contradiction. She felt an urgent, unseemly need to excuse herself to void her bladder.

Phillip Carlino was not unfamiliar with the anxiety and terror at these moments, however well-concealed. His specialization, like that of the ontologist's, stripped away pretenses, games people played. Coverups. In these visceral matters, the responses were automatic. The very words—"brain surgery"—struck cold terror, naturally, he knew. His problem was in dealing with these reactions. He found he could best serve his patients and himself by masking his feelings. His own agonies and terrors had no priority to theirs; and so he kept the straw-grasping and the "why me?" syndrome displays at arm's length. The thousand and one bargaining ploys of pathetic victims and their loved ones holding off death. And for this he had earned the reputation of "that brilliant technician," said in a way which suggested they were also thinking, what a cold fish.

"You'll cut off my hair," Connie quietly said, and those in the room knew she had begun to accept the situation.

"It'll grow back quickly," Phil said. "I'm sure you'll be just as attractive in a wig for a while."

"Let me call your people," Doctor Ephraim said.

"*No.* "

Both men were soon gone and, for the next several hours, Connie, who knew what loneliness was, had never felt lonelier. She secretly yearned to hear her mother's . . . her father's voice. Hear them just once again after all the years. Not necessarily to talk to her since they never actually said anything to her when they did talk, as she recalled it . . . just their voices. She thought even of reaching for the phone, dialing the number and hearing one of them say hello. No more.

Lying now in the darkened room she had something of an instant replay of her life. She wished she could have said she was the product of a dismal Wilkes-Barre miner's home, or been spit out of the so-called Minnesota pipeline. Then at least she could *possibly* justify much of what happened. The experts might say, "Poor, disadvantaged thing. Obviously a product of her environment." Her environment had been a twelve-room Tudor mansion on a two-acre North Shore Long Island spread. Her social pathology was nil, as a child she had everything, she knew. Popularity, looks—even brains. All the goodies.

"So what did happen?" she had asked innumerable times of herself—of many therapists. And there came many answers. Some simple. Some abtruse. Logical, even. Fitting the matrix of their particular modality whether its source was in Vienna or beyond the Himalayas. But she knew they missed the mark. It had to be, otherwise there'd have been an end to it, and there wasn't. Accepting responsibility for herself, at least blaming no one else, the anger had at least drained off some . . .

As a freshman at Sarah Lawrence, she recalled being —chuckling at the expression—deflowered. The honor went to a skinny Yale preppie with pimples on his back who had borrowed his sister's Greenwich Village flat for the occasion. She recalled lying on top of a mix of come and blood with a red Chinese-dragon kite scowling fiercely down upon her.

But even before that—when she had been fourteen—fifteen—she had become aware of the stubborn demon in her. Years later she had dubbed it the Avis Syndrome. Never first, she always came in second in everything. It didn't matter what or how hard she tried. Second was the best she could do. At riding, tennis or who would take her to the senior prom. All near misses. Second. Second best. The frustrations were awful. Shattering. Others thought she was gifted. Fortunate. And yet she agonized as her self-esteem plunged. The school counselors—even the dean—had said she should find satisfaction in her considerable accomplishments which, to anyone else, would be more than enough. But not to her. She only knew she felt an aching hollowness with each defeat. She recalled her campaigns. Sucking up to teachers. Coaches. Manipulating for position just in order to win. To no use. Even in theater arts, when her heart had been set on playing Nora or Rosalind, she could only come away with the second-banana role. One wiseacre therapist—well, who knew, maybe he had a point?—suggested that she was hopelessly acting out the childhood fate of every little girl unable to accept her role of second fiddle to mother, in competition for father. In a way, it almost made sense, but it sure as hell didn't help . . .

It was soon after the Greenwich Village fiasco when she first realized her surpassing forte. It was, simply—fucking. The prime talent was there all along, just waiting to blossom. No second fiddle about this . . . And whomever she did it with, they somehow knew what she wanted to hear. Besides, she deserved it . . . She was great. The tops. "Connie, you're terrific!" And now, lying on the hospital bed, reflecting, she realized she couldn't even recall any particular pleasure from the act itself. Her payoff would be in the ego-massage . . . "You're the greatest."

When Louis Marshall Kanebaker of Kanebaker Chemicals discovered that his only child had become a prostitute—that she was on the town, getting paid for it —that instead of indulging in sorority capers she was giving blow jobs at the Edison Hotel—he almost suffered a stroke. Never had she seen him so wild. So savaging. Even if he had been told what she discovered years later, that she had merely inherited his own drive—that she worshipped at another altar in the temple of his bitch goddess, success, he would not have heard. He would not have understood . . .

The hospital machinery moved inexorably. Down in the basement of the large facility, one of the battery of Xerox machines, somewhere between suggestions for the dieticians for next week's menu and an announcement to the staff residents of a lecture on the healing properties of laughter, a few copies of an operating room schedule were spat out:

TIME	O.R.	PATIENT	UNIT	PROCEDURE
8:00 A.M.	6	Constance Keenan	1 So.	Exploratory

SURGEON	ASSISTANT	ANESTHETIST
Dr. Phillip Carlino	Dr. Lewis Aarons	Dr. Jules Wise

REMARKS
Age: 28; possible tumor excision

The operation following hers was asterisked on the schedule as noncommital, which meant that if complications developed during hers, this one would be bumped to another time.

Beneath the frenzied activity of the large hospital

there was a running undercurrent of security. A logic, a sense of accountability. It was partially what allowed a patient, as he attached the plastic ID, to surrender— turn over a large part of his will and be engulfed in the routine . . . Connie's room had become her own private universe. Word had gone out to several of her friends, and flowers and chocolates and candied fruit began to appear with cautious get-well cards. She understood the caution—the need for it. She occupied a special, exotic place among the men who knew her. She was the vessel —the guardian—of some unsavory and potentially even dangerous secrets.

Dr. Phillip Carlino appeared a few times, lastly to explain what was to happen the following morning. His voice was as remote and detached, she thought, as if he were lecturing a group of interns. She was lying in her own pajamas.

He stopped abruptly. "You're not listening," he said.

"No."

He began to get up from the vinyl chair. "I'll come by later."

"No, *wait.*" There was a moment's silence. Their eyes held. "I'm a hooker, y'know."

Silence. A cruise ship somewhere downriver boomed its whistle as it cast off its last line. A panic came over her. Why the hell did she say it? Why now? Did it have to do with the new excitement she'd been feeling when he came into the room? She didn't think so. He triggered something else in her . . . What? She went down the checklist of what in men turned her on. He undoubtedly had his dark, macho attractions, but she knew better. That couldn't be it. Not for these feelings, not here, not now. Was she doing the number, she wondered, endowing her doctor with godlike infallibility? Other women did. That, too, she rejected. She only knew for certain some inner voice was saying, Careful here, lady.

"So, you're a hooker," he quietly repeated with a hint of mocking in his voice.

Good old Doctor Ephraim told him, she thought, as if what was ailing her was an occupational hazard.

"You've known some," she said. "Hookers, I mean."

"I've known some."

"Any like me? Like dynamite, I mean, doctor?"

For the first time she saw him, and heard him laugh, and liked what she saw and heard. He had become a person, not some automaton. His eyes softened. What was behind them—that scrim—fell away. The phone beside her bed tinkled softly.

"For you," she said.

He said a series of yesses into the instrument, but soon she became aware of several subtle changes he was undergoing. A certain tension. The spatula fingers of the hand on the table were tapping at it nervously. His face was averted, and yet she knew it was expressing an irritation. Why had he turned away? Was it to avoid her eyes? That by-now familiar terror returned, chilling her. She was absolutely certain the call had to do with her.

He replaced the instrument. "I'll be back in a while," he said.

"Forget a sponge in someone?" she called after him.

He turned, startled; then, realizing it was a joke, turned again and was gone.

Something was wrong. Absolute certainty settled down over her. But what? She avoided the litany of possibilities since there could be no end. No, there was an end. Her end. The terminal end.

Bad usage, Connie. And for a Sarah Lawrence girl at that . . . The tears came to her eyes, and she was only grateful that there was nobody there to see them . . .

CHAPTER TWO

PHIL CARLINO was familiar with many of his mother's quaint Sicilian superstitions. He not only knew them, he found them occurring to him at the most inappropriate moments. He thought of one now: "The first worry of the day becomes a regret." It left him uneasy.

That morning he had awakened earlier than usual. A worrisome procedure was scheduled for eight, and a succession of possible complications flashed through his mind, depressing him.

The evening before, at Ann Samish's small dinner party which he knew she had arranged for his benefit, he anything but sparkled. Ann, a voguish interior decorator, had chosen her guests carefully; the conversation was witty, delicious as the food. Throughout, he had sat unresponsive and heavy despite her best efforts to involve him. The bright talk just flowed about him as if he were a log snagged at the bottom of a fast-flowing stream. He could do nothing about it either. Someone would be telling of a backgammon ploy and his thoughts were on managing a surgical section of the commissure involving the *corpus callosum*. The incident at a disco between Truman and a notorious lesbian known as the Bitch of Olympic Towers regaled the table. Phil was meanwhile manipulating his probe through the parietal region. It was a trade-off: clearing the traumatized area could mean the patient's life against the loss of speech.

Later, saying good night, Ann had slipped him the apartment key, whispering, ". . . no more than an hour."

He sat at a small corner of the Regency lounge, sipping a Perrier. The black Formica table before him held an imagined chart of the human brain as he visualized his invasion of it. He prepared his strategy for tomorrow. A general marshaling of his forces and what he knew of the enemy, in this case the infinite variations of the brain which could frustrate and undo him by the slightest anomaly.

An hour and a half later he slipped into the dramatically furnished but now darkened bedroom, and unhurriedly undressed. The lovely woman in his arms—warm, eager and expectant—became aware his endearments were flat, his foreplay mechanical.

"Do me a favor, darling," she said at one point. "Get dressed and get the hell out of here." It was said lightly, more with understanding than anger. It bespoke a familiarity, an untapped reservoir of goodwill earned for better times. Kissing her gratefully, he dressed quickly and left.

He lived in two floors of a modernized brownstone in the upper Fifties just off Madison Avenue. It was tastily furnished, mostly in Ann Samish's taste, but with contributions from other women who would have liked to take over caring for him. But this was satisfactorily done by Fanny, his housekeeper of several years.

Fanny knew his moods, where everything should be;

and her efficiency was exceeded only by the good humor which left her only with the appearance of Phil's mother, who made it a practice of regularly "stopping in." While the Sicilian woman looked and poked about, muttering fierce, foreign things, Fanny went into that impervious shell of shuffling "Yas ma'ams"; but the moment the woman closed the door behind her, she raged and vented her fury, tossing about things which only a few moments ago she had neatly set down. She'd then storm out for the uptown trip home on the Madison Avenue bus in which, God forbid, someone should jostle her or not yield space enough for her to sit properly.

Maria Carlino made the uptown journey from her old Mulberry Street tenement out of a very real worry for "her Felipe." *La strega negra* will poison her boy, she maintained to her husband, a disabled, pensioned ex-police sergeant. "She'll poison him with the food he eats from a glass table!"

Maria Carlino had been born in that same tenement sixty years ago, and yet she appeared no different than her mother, an emigrant from Palermo. Incredibly, almost, she had spent her life maintaining the old culture and resisting the new. Her "tragedy" now was the invasion of "the neighborhood" by "the ethnics," as the politicos politely called them. Her prayers in church were mainly for her son: that the blessed Mary help him withstand the temptations of his life-style. Once she came upon a frozen pizza in his refrigerator. Frozen pizza! The mozarella—the funghi and pomodoro seemed appealing enough on the cardboard cover. But that was devil's work! Inside was garbage! And into the garbage it went.

The two women hated each other with equal fervor. The bitter-tongued Sicilian out of jealousy and xenophobia. *La strega* wasn't even Catholic! But the measure of Fanny's affection for her "professor" was her endurance of his mother. Moreover, Phil had once taken her grandson out of a city hospital ward and saved his life. This alone made it possible for her to endure the "old bitch from downtown" and even to doing his windows.

After a missing slipper Phil recognized other signs that his mother had visited the day before. No bath towels where bath towels should be. Even the water-pic mouthpiece was somehow missing, and the water squirted over the bathroom. Then, not a speck of coffee anywhere, not even instant. And in searching the shelves, a box of Twinkies or something fell and scattered over the floor. Fanny's temper tantrum was in evidence everywhere.

And I'm doing brain surgery in an hour, he thought in dismay. He was tempted to phone and cancel the operation, that or have someone cover for him.

The surgery began according to schedule with no indication of anything unusual. Standing in the background, his gloved hands beneath a towel, he watched as the patient was draped and prepped. His glance took in the oscilloscope blips. The anesthesiologist had adjusted his mix of halothane, nitrous oxide, and oxygen and seemed to be satisfied as he adjusted the mask and put the patient under. Vital signs were established within normal parameters. Two cc's of a 0.2 percent succinylcholine chloride solution through the I.V. had paralyzed the skeletal muscles. The placement of the endotracheal tube followed. The anesthesiologist then nodded to Phil, who stepped forward and took his place at the shaved, immobilized head which was to be his field.

The patient, a forty-six-year-old black male with a motor paralysis of the right side attributed to a fall from a painter's scaffold, bore the first half of the operation satisfactorily. A complication then arose, something totally unexpected, even though Phil was aware the unexpected was to be expected, the abnormal among the bil-

lions of brain cells constituting the human brain altogether normal. The neurosurgeon confronted and had to
contend with these unexpected events and anomalies.
Even his high-powered optic viewer was a crude instrument, making him little better than some early astrolo-
ger peering at the heavens through a primitive telescope.
The microscopic details of the human brain, different,
distinct and individual as snowflakes or fingerprints,
were in a sense as much a mystery.

The clock said an hour and forty-two minutes of
elapsed time. It was then patient Dennis Jefferson began
to sour. A tiny fragment of bone, shattered in the accident, had somehow punctured a tiny arteriole in such a
manner that it blocked off hemorrhaging. And yet the
jagged bit of bone impinged upon a complex of neurons
and synapses effecting the proper passage of messages to
various motor nerves, which in turn ran to several muscles. Phil's anxiety increased as he realized removal of
the bone splinter could start a bleeder that would be
almost impossible to shut off unless he approached it by
a hazardous rerouting of the probe.

It was a life-threatening decision, one of several. And
it had to be done. The bone could jar loose at some future
time and Mr. Jefferson would be dead in moments. For
the next several hours Phil Carlino and his team worked
as a wondrously precise machine. The only sound was
the clatter of instruments on the Mayo stand, the beep
of the heart monitor and the hiss of the respiratory apparatus. Nurses dabbed the foreheads of the surgical team
more and more frequently as each of their moves created
situations requiring new decisions and new moves. They
worked deliberately. Unhurriedly. Their economy of
movement wasted no second, and in that sense it was,
indeed, an art form.

Dennis Jefferson's vital signs stabilized, and in a short
while his life and normal future became assured. Back-

ing away from the table, Phil turned over the "closing up" to the surgical resident.

But the day was not done. He had by now forgotten the adage of the day's first worry; nevertheless, more trouble lay ahead.

It began with the phone message in Connie Keenan's room. By the time he reached the administrator's office in the first floor he had developed a good head of steam. What he had heard was outrageous. Barging past the astonished secretary in the outer office, he confronted Doctor Joseph Annin.

The administrator was a pale, thin neurasthenic from whom life was being bleached away by the vicissitudes of running an institution this size with its awesome complexities. The light eyes behind rimless spectacles seemed actually surprised and offended by the daily assaults upon him; his pinched features and bluish lips would have warned the greenest intern that Doctor Joseph Annin was an imminent candidate for an infarct. Despite Phil's state of mind, he unconsciously registered the Third Avenue bartender's diagnosis. "The elevens are showing"—this referring to the accentuated throat cords in someone morbidly afflicted.

As Phil read the proferred message, Doctor Annin waved off his secretary standing at the threshold, poised to summon security.

Phil looked up. His voice was calm. "What does it mean?"

"What it says. Your patient's to be sent forthwith with her records to Elias Nunn Center in Southern California."

Phil was perplexed. "She's my patient—"

"No one questions that, doctor."

"But this"—Phil waved the message—"I've never heard of such a thing—"

"Frankly, doctor, neither have I."

"So then we ignore it," Phil said. "The operation goes on as scheduled."

Joseph Annin solemnly shook his head. "Not in this hospital, I'm afraid."

The importance of the name on the wire wasn't lost on Phil; and yet his experience in Vietnam had inured him to orders from high command. In charge of a front-line hospital unit, he had come to realize such directives often created more confusion than incoming fire; hence he usually disregarded them. Tossing the message across the desk, he said, "She will not be shipped *anywhere*. At this moment a cancer may be growing in her head—"

"With all respect, doctor, you apparently miss the point."

"What point?"

"Doctor Nunn is interested in your patient, and Doctor Nunn . . ." He didn't complete the sentence. He didn't have to. His gesture, the near-awe with which he said the name conjured up a very special person.

Phil, of course, knew of the eminent man. Who in his profession didn't regard this distinguished scientist in the highest esteem?

Rubbing his chin, Phil said, "Nunn—"

"Yes?"

"He's mostly a research man."

"And a neurosurgeon."

"Did you see the workup on Miss Keenan?" Phil asked, going on to say he considered her a run-of-the-mill tumor resection. "We don't even seriously suspect malignancy."

"Nevertheless—"

"What?"

"He's requested her."

"But it doesn't make sense—"

"No, it doesn't . . . and by the way, your diagnosis was correct."

"How do you know?" Phil asked sharply.

"I took the liberty of presenting the case to the surgical board."

"You—" Phil was so astounded he could only stare in astonishment.

"And the mystery remains," Doctor Annin continued, "why the superstar of neurosurgery wants your patient shipped crosscountry to perform what you consider the equivalent of a tonsilectomy."

"He doesn't get her," Phil said flatly.

Dr. Annin didn't quarrel. The room was silent. Phones outside rang, and someone had the good sense not to interrupt. Joseph Annin felt more weary than he ever had in his life as he sat in his chair, which through the years had grown larger and larger, or himself smaller. He wasn't thinking of the young doctor before him, or his patient, or even of Elias Nunn. He was thinking of himself, crouched in a foetal position in his favorite spot between rocks and hard places. He was thinking of a Latin book he had once had as a student. There was a photo of the statue of Laocoön wrestling with the serpent, its many coils entwined about him. The serpent to him was Washington; the coils, the directives, questionnaires and regulations. Reams of paper. But he and the hospital were one, the same. And they were strangled by paper serpents, and death was the simple cutting off of funds which kept such a facility alive.

"Why her?" Phil was demanding to know.

"I've thought of the computer," Annin said helplessly.

Phil regarded him for several moments. "What computer?"

The hospital superintendent sighed as he explained that it had been standard practice following instructions from Washington. "Data on all candidates for neurosurgery is to be transmitted to Washington, fed into their bank. I happen to know all hospitals in the area follow the procedure." It had been going on for months, he added.

"My patients?" Phil said, disbelieving.

"All patients," was the reply. "An automatic process."

Phil was astonished. His adrenalin churned. He could only think back to the Mulberry Street days when preparations had to be made to fight off a marauding gang from another neighborhood. He reached for the phone.

"I want to know more about this," he said quietly.

Something snapped in Joseph Annin, a sort of synergistic overload, the point when a man says, Enough already. He rose slowly from behind the desk. "You do that," he said. "Help yourself, doctor. On a good day my diastolic is a hundred and five. You wish to make it a hundred and six? I say, screw you, doctor."

Phil accepted the challenge. Referring to the name on the wire, he took up the phone and had no trouble reaching Washington, even the agency involved. Then his troubles began. He experienced a classic runaround, until finally the best he could accomplish was reaching someone three rungs removed from the man he had originally asked for. The voice was cold, indifferent, highly unimpressed with Phil's name or title. His arrogance was in direct proportion to the authority behind the directive which he regarded as graven in stone in fiery letters.

"Why?" Phil asked, "would Doctor Nunn be interested in my patient who's anything but extraordinary according to workup? And what has Doctor Nunn got to do with Washington?"

Silence at the other end.

When the man again spoke, the voice was even more robot-like.

"I'm sorry, doctor," he said. "The instructions are unequivocal. They're to be followed at once."

Phil exploded. The missing slipper—the Twinkies on

the floor—the water-pic brush missing—his near miss at surgery—now this. The tensions of a bad day was a gathering of storm clouds and the thunderbolt was inevitable. Joseph Annin stood by, admiring this outburst, this sort of venting. By some osmotic process, he even felt better. But after a few moments of unrelieved street language, Phil, realizing the futility of it, violently threw the instrument at the startled administrator, who fumbled with it a moment and listened.

"This is Doctor Annin," he said. After several moments of listening he replaced the instrument on the desk. He actually smiled at Phil. "Well, my friend, you really did it." And the administrator explained that Connie Keenan was to be placed under guard until other arrangements were made, also that he himself was expected to persuade her to accept the situation, particularly since no other doctor or hospital would accept her.

"This is . . . criminal!" Phil shouted.

Annin agreed. "And while you prove that, doctor," he said, "remember what you yourself said . . . 'A cancer *may* be growing in her head.' Also remember that the best neurosurgeon in the world is available to remove it. At once, I presume."

For Connie, the long habit of living didn't easily accommodate the possibility of her dying. The hospital atmosphere itself created if not a paranoia in the seriously ill, certainly a solipsism. Self-centeredness was naturally incubated here. You became the center of the universe, the hub of all life and activity. It was that way with her, particularly in view of Phil Carlino's strange behavior and subsequent events. She was reminded of a girl she once did conventions with . . . Gladys or Ginger or something. She recalled her comment after a hard night with a hotel full of randy orthodontists: Don't take life too seriously. You'll never get out of it alive. Ha.

The door opened several times, but no Doctor Carlino returning as he said he would. Nor was it the anesthetist, as he had said. The first was a kindly old lady in a neat gray uniform who sweetly asked if she'd like something to read. Then a man with mop and pail.

I'm terminal! she thought hysterically, yet the friggin' floors must shine!

She reached for the phone. Call Doctor Ephraim, she thought. He'll straighten it all out. One call from him— She changed her mind. She thought of Sylvia. A little gossip. A few laughs was what she needed to get off this wild anxiety which was no stranger to her. Her fears were illogical. Weren't they always?

"What do you mean the phone is out of order?" she screamed at the operator.

At this point, Doctor Joseph Annin entered the room, smiling. The anesthetist, she thought. At last. Things were on track again.

The hospital administrator introduced himself and almost at once there was another plucking of her tautened nerves. She disliked the man at once, less for his professional sleekness and too-strong cologne than for the fact she recognized her new friend, Fear, standing at his elbow. Despite his smiling.

"I'm honored, doctor," she said. "The superintendent, my goodness! Are you about to ask me for my eyes or kidneys in case, y'know?"

He laughed, showing a too perfect set of bridgework. "You've heard of Doctor Elias Nunn," he said. "The Nobel Prize winner."

"He marches for the ecology," she recalled, wondering what this was now.

Doctor Annin again laughed. "He also saves people. As a doctor, I mean." He drew the chair closer to the bed. "Doctor Nunn has become interested in you."

"In me?"

"In your case."

"I have a surgeon."

"Indeed you have," the administrator said, adding quickly, "and a good—an excellent one!"

"So what are we talking about?"

He leaned closer as if to establish an intimacy. "My dear," he began, "if I or anyone dear to me required neurosurgery, I'd want—I probably wouldn't get, but I'd want—"

"Elias Nunn?"

Who else? He then launched into superlatives enumerating but a few of the great man's accomplishments, most of which she couldn't comprehend, but at any moment she half expected a claim that the man in California had something to do with the parting of the Red Sea.

She interrupted. "You didn't hear what I said. I have a doctor. An excellent doctor, you admit."

Annin knew he had to be careful here. He had the ethical responsibility not to denigrate another physician. He carefully skirted these shoals. "There is good, and there is the best," he said. He had noted Connie's silk pajamas, the label of the robe thrown across the foot of the bed. "If I said Bergdorf's vis-à-vis Gimbels?"

"Has this been discussed with Doctor Carlino?"

"Of course!"

"What does he say?"

"Doctor Carlino? What *can* he say?"

"What *did* he say?"

"He concurs."

"I should be operated on by this—"

"Doctor Nunn. Elias Nunn. Yes."

One instinct in Connie had been sharpened by the vagaries of her life—she knew bullshit when she was confronted with it, and at this moment she knew, she was certain, the smiling little man before her had a bad case of wet armpits.

In a short while she was alone again. Alone also with thoughts piling up, one on another. What was going on? Who was manipulating? Someone possibly meant well for her. Who? At the very top of the list was her father. Had Ephraim somehow, despite her orders, discovered her identity, and in the light of the seriousness of the situation got in touch with him? He could afford—would certainly want the very best medical care for her. Nothing but the best, and that would mean that California hotshot. But, no. It wasn't her father's style. He'd come to her first. Say how he felt. Reconcile. So then who else? It was baffling, too baffling. If there was any value in it at all it was to divert her momentarily from her condition.

Phil canceled his rounds, and even his clinic, an event in itself. He was no less at a loss for an explanation than his patient. He at least was more familiar with hospital procedures and administrative snafus, but this was unheard of. To his confusion, anger was shortly added. A smoldering anger that he barely succeeded in checking. He had outgrown many things from his heritage, but not an antipathy to authority. Anyone with any knowledge of Phil Carlino would say he was not one to push around. His very appearance said as much. During his school and college years, even at Northwestern where he had taken his degree, he had been involved in activist movements, and on several occasions it was only his scholastic excellence that saved his skin. At medical school one of the very first principles drilled into him was that a doctor's patient was his and his alone. The relationship was inviolate. Grounds for interference, especially by government, were severely limited. Gross negligence or even misconduct had their slow, ponderous machinery. For another physician to take over a patient with government sanction and aid was unheard of. He couldn't begin to cope with it. Was Connie Keenan perhaps the girl-friend of someone very high up who could apply this pressure? An Arab shiek, maybe? Non-compliance would mean an oil embargo? Crazy!

The administrator's threats hadn't been empty. Phil called several hospitals where he had courtesy. The reaction was immediate. Excuses, excuses . . . he tried to turn Connie over to several of his colleagues—he came up against a stone wall there, too.

Frustrated, bone-weary, it was early evening before he returned to the hospital. Almost the entire day had been spent on the Keenan affair, and if anything, he knew less about it than before.

He found her staring out the window. It was night outside, the grime of the window was streaked by the soft drizzle. Phil noticed the dinner tray, untouched, and what was on it surely not pre-op. As she turned about at his entrance, he saw at once the tension.

"Well," she said, "a man of his word."

He came to the point at once. He had made up his mind to do this during the taxi ride uptown; he'd shuffle his priorities. His first responsibility was to her need for immediate surgery. What was in her brain could be nothing—a harmless, easily excised growth, but then again there was always the possibility of a gliablastoma or something equally ominous in which a sloughed-off cell could doom her.

"I've news," he began.

"The same good news I have?" Without waiting for his reply, she went on, "Who's this Doctor Nunn?"

He realized the situation had already been put to her, probably by the administrator himself. "The very best neurosurgeon in the world."

She studied him closely for several moments. "You're saying, are you, that I should do what they say."

"Yes. You couldn't be better served—"

"Not even by you?"

"Not even by me, or anyone else." He went on to explain that Doctor Nunn's facility was in California. "I expect you won't have to worry about transportation. Which brings up another matter. I don't work for nothing."

"I didn't expect you did," she said testily. "And are you suggesting Doctor Nunn will?"

Phil shrugged. "I shouldn't worry about it." Suddenly he smiled. "You said you're dynamite. Maybe he heard—"

She got up. "You asshole, this is my *life*. My head's to be opened." And then she was saying in a more reasonable tone, "The sixty-four-thousand-dollar question . . . why? Why is everyone so nice to me? Especially Superdoc in California?"

She wanted it straight, he thought, she'd have it. "I don't know."

For a long moment she studied him. Then, reaching for the phone, she asked for Doctor Annin. It took only a moment for her to reach him, which Phil thought remarkable in itself. But not as remarkable as what followed.

"I agree to go to your Doctor Nunn," she said to the official, "on one condition. Doctor Carlino goes with me."

Phil could hear the garbled protests at the other end. Her expression didn't change as she listened patiently. Phil thought it was surely a joke, a ploy . . . the notion was absurd, impossible. He didn't for a moment accept it as a serious threat. "If not," she went on, "you can forget it." She hung up and turned toward Phil.

He was smiling indulgently. "Why in the world did you say a thing like that?"

"Because I meant it."

And he could now see she did. "Now look here, I can understand your apprehension—"

"*Can* you, doctor?"

Trying to keep calm, he explained the impossibility of the idea . . . there was his schedule, the patients under his care, the responsibilities . . .

She listened impassively. When he was through, she said, "Now you go home and pack your little bag."

"Like hell I will—"

"Will they chloroform me then? Ship me in ice?"

It took Phil twenty-four hours to realize that when a high authority in government decided to exert its will, there was precious little its target (victim?) could do. Violence or the threat of it wasn't necessary. Forgotten regulations and codes were trundled out for bureaucrats to enforce. All very legal, very proper . . . there it is, written . . . the law. And the errand boys were even worse than the bosses . . . awash in moral rectitude and posturing, blank faces, as they went about pursuing the letter of the law, to the death of its spirit. Phil quickly found himself deluged in tax problems, drug prescription investigations, his office X-ray was even adjudged dangerous in voltage. In twenty-four hours he was obliged to have his secretary pass the word along that he would accompany Miss Keenan to the Elias Nunn Center of Behavioral Sciences in Southern California.

CHAPTER THREE

DOCTOR ELIAS NUNN had won his Nobel Prize for his "elucidation of brain synaptic responses," which in layman's terms was his explanation of his studies of the brain's transmitter substances, the messengers that activate the complex organ. He had determined why, in some instances, the transmission is chemical, in others electrical.

He was now in Washington, where he was to receive still another testimonial to his genius, with his attractive young wife Tessa.

The auditorium at the National Institute for Scientific Research and Development was almost entirely filled. The audience included distinguished scientists, specialists in many modalities, also brought here for the occasion. These represented various universities, several think-tanks and a number of research and development facilities associated with various large corporations. Many knew of each other, their specialties and their present work, from published papers as well as the scientific grapevine. There were friends, colleagues and not a few competitors, even enemies. Their own scientific opinions were often held with a zealot's singlemindedness—a conviction that theirs was the true religion. Personal envy was another matter . . . a new book becoming successful was secretly envied yet quietly derided as "popular stuff." The sharpest cleavage was between those in "pure" science—abstract research—and those in applied science, teaching or consulting. All were there at the invitation of the head of an important government agency, and almost all who were invited came. It wasn't so much to hear the tiresome succession of speeches, or for the bad punch or tired canapés at a flurry of receptions; but not to be invited—not to be seen, or preferably heard—could be a chilling omen for the future. Faculty boards with life and death power over tenure, as well as corporate executives, held an uncanny sense of knowing the status of their people in their establishment; invitations to such functions mattered a great deal.

Eli Nunn sat at the center of the dais as the guest of honor, his wife beside him. On either side, in some arbitrary pecking order, was an array of government people into health care or science, three university presidents and a sprinkling of other Nobel laureates. It was noted that nowhere to be seen in the assemblage was a single military uniform, this out of deference to Doctor Nunn's well-known stance toward war and the people who made it their business . . . the famed, or according to your viewpoint, infamous so-called military-industrial complex.

The tall spare body, familiar from much press and television coverage, sat erect as the speakers at the lectern took their turns in praise of him. His large head, with unkempt graying hair, had the look of an oldish Byron, lean and somehow hungry about the jaw. He kept his gaze lowered as if uncomfortable with the heated-up superlatives directed at him. He appeared to be scrutinizing his long fingers, splotched with an old lab man's inevitable nitric-acid stains. It was an admirable show of humility on his part as a colleague of years recounted his contributions in the field of transmitter substances both excitory and inhibitory, with occasional passing reference to the field of Evoked Potentials.

His practiced performance came easily to Eli, whose thoughts were elsewhere. He had no illusions about the purpose of the affair, which he graciously put up with. Then, too, there was the residual attraction that Tessa, new to this, was enjoying it enormously; it also magnified his stature in her eyes. Nevertheless, he was very much aware that this and all to follow had been set up because of a report from California that he was waffling again in his commitment to "the program." Which was true, he realized. His doubts and enthusiasms ebbed and flowed like the tides below their cliffside house.

". . . irrepressible genius . . . our foremost treasure for his pioneering in the field of neurophysiology . . ." Heads in the audience nodded, faces smiled in approval, but these were more mechanical than sincere. They were, he knew, mostly thinking of their own work, or personal affairs . . . returning that broken grouter to Sears . . . how do I flunk that girl I've been sleeping with, or do I? . . . The speaker was mentioning names such as Eccles, Marchbanks, Penfield . . . likening Eli Nunn to them, and the linkage to these giants caused a restless stirring. He was going too far, some thought, carried away with his own eloquence. It was Caesar being offered a kingly crown, nominated for godhood. Yet it went on and on, a parade of speakers showering accolade upon accolade. At any moment, Eli expected a choral *te deum laudamus.*

Eli had speculated why none of the five members of the government's Committee of Bio-Energetic Affairs were present. These men, none scientists, had been chosen to represent the government's interest within the consortium which funded the Elaine Frumkin Institute, of which the Elias Nunn Center was the essential part but whose true role was hidden beneath the general term of Behavioral Studies. He concluded it had been decided among themselves that their presence would be a discordant note among the scientists and scholars. Everything so well planned, he thought. Haven't missed a beat. Not even his Achilles heel of weakness to flattery. Especially not.

Tessa reached over and took his hand in hers, breaking up his thoughts. Turning his head to her, he smiled his wry smile, suggesting how could anyone possibly see such things in him?

"I feel like I'm attending my own funeral," he said in a low voice.

Despite Eli's hunger for the spotlight, he was also a decent man with perspective. He didn't feel any particular guilt or conflict about his need, fairly common among those with the gift of public personality. He suspected that men in the highest places accepted and sought suicidal jobs—including the Presidency itself—out of such ego need.

Elias Nunn was known for more than his profound knowledge of neurophysiology and his virtuosity at the operating table. He also had considerable political charisma, having been something of a guru for the young. During the turbulent sixties he was at or near the forefront of numerous anti-war protests, to the embarrassment of his establishment—academic as well as scientific, which regarded itself above the fray. And yet he was sincere as well as courageous, never wavering before pressures that at times became formidable. He pursued his conscience with a boldness, a tenacity and a singlemindedness characteristic of him in the labs or at the operating table; his winning of the Nobel Prize augmented his popularity and with it the demand for his appearance at progressive functions, or at least the use of his name.

Sitting on the dais, depicted as a super-patriot, he couldn't avoid the ironic thought that a short distance away was the FBI building bearing the name of the man who had regarded him as a near traitor; and in the same building was probably a file characterizing him as some sort of threat to the national interest.

He thought of the reception in the White House rose garden as the cherry on the frosting on the cake. The ultimate ego massage . . . How, indeed, could he not return to the Center, recharged, to conduct more experiments upon human beings? Wasn't he a hero, even—that absurd phrase—a national treasure? Of course the men at the lectern, bespeaking their practiced rhetoric, didn't quite know what he knew. They hadn't seen his failures. Yet even if they had, someone would have sought to reassure him, say, "Did any of the scientific pioneers— the giants of the past—stroll easily into their triumphs? They too suffered many setbacks, casualties." He had his casualties, all right, and the pain wasn't theirs alone. He did share it. How often was he told—did he need to hear? —that it was a small price he *and* they were paying for a kind of immortality . . . a guarantee of survival in the minds of men, and so forth . . . But he was restless with this convenient, soothing rationale directed at him ceaselessly by Norville Kondorf, the man selected by the committee to oversee the program and ride herd on him.

It was the sort of spring day when the nation's capital put on its gala outfit. The blossoms were in full bloom, and the weather warmly delightful. The White House rose garden was redolent with gay party sounds and the tinkling of glasses crested with blue Presidential seals. It was an exquisitely groomed affair, the scene reminiscent of a Monet palette, the bright colors dancing on points of warm light.

". . . and our sources inform us Professor Rikovski at the Leningrad Institute has been reporting progress in cortical stimulation of the brain . . ."

Eli turned a bleak glance on the young State Department official who had just nervously uttered this. He had been watching his wife Tessa and the young couple she was in animated conversation with. As he sipped the California champagne he had been thinking that the bearded young fellow, or even his friend, were involved in molecular physics or something as arcane, and were on loan to some agency or other as consultants. This was a town of consultants, and it brought to mind a marvelous story he had once been told by a Professor Albert Salvatori in Rome that reflected his own view of Washington and its consultants . . .

It seemed that certain Roman ruins had become the habitat of abandoned cats. The Council for the Preservation of Roman Ruins met in urgent session when an explosion in the cat population was noted. The single cause was discovered to be a male tom who was given the name Serafino. Serafino became the toast of Rome. Jokes were invented, ballads sung in honor of Serafino's prowess with the girls. But the Council had its worries. What to do about the overspilling cat population? Poisoning Serafino, shooting him—these were discussed but quickly discarded as political suicide. Serafino was too beloved. It was finally decided to send a vet down into the ruins one dark night and castrate the over-endowed culprit. And this was done. Shortly after, it was noticed that Serafino hadn't changed, at least in style. He strutted about as importantly as ever. A male cat, curious, approached Serafino and said, "Serafino, tell me. How is it after the terrible thing that was done to you, as everyone knows, the removal of those magnificent jewels—

that you don't hide in shame? You still walk about puffed up as ever?" Serafino winked at the inquisitive cat and said, "My friend, I have become a consultant." . . .

The State Department youth in his Brooks Brothers summer seersucker complete with white shirt, buttoned-down collar, appeared earnest enough, and Eli wondered if even this eager young character was there to nudge him onward . . . no, certainly not, he decided. There went his damn paranoia again—

"We've every confidence, sir," the young man went on, "you'll have us there first."

Not paranoia. Eli directed at the young man what was known by his staff as "the laser look" as he said, "Has the program become a Sputnik contest?"

Eli then quickly turned from him, thinking, Why am I so uptight about this? It's true . . . the prospectus for the fundings, written by myself, for God's sake, implied just that. The Soviets *are* far ahead of us in the field . . .

Although the program had been proposed as pure science—basic research—only a fool would have missed the implications that with a breakthrough in the higher psychological processes would come inestimable rewards in commercial, political and even strategic areas. The human brain was in effect a reservoir of untold weath and power. He recalled how for a long time the funding had been stalled. "Too esoteric," "Too arcane," the words came back.

He wasn't chagrined at the time. History was merely repeating itself. England after the French Revolution experienced decades of reactionary attitudes toward science, cutting itself off from the important scientific ideas burgeoning on the continent out of fear of political contagion. When he spoke about the work by Vygotsky and Luria, Washington yawned. "More Eli Nunn and his radical ideas."

It took, ironically but not surprisingly, the CIA to get the cortical stimulation program off the ground. A secret intelligence report was received that it was true, the Soviets had given cortical stimulation not only high priority but even the military was involved. Purse strings were untied. A consortium of government and several multinationals was hurriedly put together, and the program was off.

From a sort of radical, if talented, troublemaker, Eli's status did a one-hundred-and-eighty-degree turn. He became "the Beethoven of the brain"; someone even called him another Einstein. He was bemused by the irony of it all, and yet he loved it. He went to California, and in the name of science performed their work in a place especially built for him, the Elias Nunn Center of Behavioral Science—

There was a stir. Conversation stopped. Eyes turned toward the balcony. The President of the United States, his wife and retinue were about to descend to the garden.

To see, to speak to him, Eli thought. The President of the United States . . . He reviewed in his mind the great men he had met through the years, but the President of the United States had a genuinely special, nearly exalted meaning for him . . . Oh, pop, wherever you are, your attention please! See this. This is Eli. Your Eli whom you had written off. I could never throw that damned football spiral good enough for you or handle a Stilson wrench the way you could with your big, gnarled hands, but the President of the United States is on his way down to shake *my* hand. So admit you were wrong, pop . . . pop? . . . Such feeling rarely came out in so many words, but they were there, deeply imbedded in his psyche as always, nagging him, pursuing him, never mind his logical realization that his father in worldly terms had been a mediocre, even failed man who had died at the same Bridgeport, Connecticut lathe that he knew and understood better than his family. . . .

Later in the elegant hotel suite overlooking Rock Creek Park, Eli and Tessa were resting for a final evening function before their departure in the morning. It was to be a dinner hosted by the same agency head who had signed a directive to a New York hospital putting a hold on a woman no one had ever heard of.

He lay on the rumpled bed where they had just made love as Tessa moved unself-consciously nude about the room. A beautiful, strong body . . . his heart ached with the thought of her youth, with remembering the delicious smooth feel of her skin, her firm, full-nippled breasts. He watched her hips, sprocketed in some special way to delight. The body was hers, and yet in some way his, and it made him feel less unhappy with what fifty-four years had done to his. She had good bones, as the photographers said, and straw-blonde hair, only slightly less dark than that below, which had the smell of good earth, that Minnesota earth she'd come from. The rounded fullness and beauty of her reminded him of the old WPA murals so fashionable when he was a boy, the one, for example, that filled the wall of the downtown main post office in his town.

He loved her. He truly loved her, but in a different way than he had loved Laura, that good, self-effacing woman whose life orbited around him and his needs—until it was taken by cancer almost two years ago. Laura had given up her own career as a biochemist to serve him better, and serve him she did. She saw to his appointments and speaking engagements, supported him in his frequent bouts with trustees and administrators. She listened to his research problems, half the time not quite understanding what he was saying, but she knew that his being able to speak about them in itself often provided him with a flash of insight. Tessa could never fill that gap for him, but she gave him another love, one of piquant lightness and music. The house as well as his life became filled with these things, although Laura had kept them both unquestionably neater. . . .

I love that man, that beautiful man . . . Tessa had thought such thoughts that day almost a year ago at the anti-nuclear demonstration at the university where she had been preparing her Ph.D. on the music of Palestrina. She loved him. She knew this although she had stood at least two hundred yards from him on the crowded track field. He was speaking over a p.a. system. Saying the things the young audience already knew but wanted to hear from *him*. From anyone, but especially from him. He was so clear and direct, zeroing in with precise words to the very heart of an issue. He seemed to have a special aura. Her head swam with the excitement of hearing the words from him like a revelation. As if her feeling for him was a revelation. She made up her mind to meet him, and made it her business to. It was later that same day in a crowded motel room. The wine, the talk were good. Heady. Hours later they found themselves somehow alone; and in a totally natural acquiescence, as if it had happened a hundred times before, they took off their clothes and went to bed. . . .

Eli recognized in Tessa the reverse of the same coin. Truth in an almost childlike quintessence. It was manifest in the things she said, in how she said them. Even in how she looked. Her large gray eyes spaced wide that peered at you and you had no will to lie to them.

Truth was, after all, especially important to Eli, even then. He sought it in his work, his political alignments and his commitment to it when it wasn't popular. But during the year of his involvement he suffered as he realized his work—what it did to some people—was also in its fashion a betrayal of the truth. It became a nagging, persistent thing, one that wouldn't be pushed back however he had tried. Only Tessa stayed pure, the same, and for this he clung, loved her even more, as if he could somehow tap into her ample store of it. . . .

Now she was sitting at the edge of the bed in Washington, leaning over to kiss him, and as her hair flooded over his face and body he thought, gratefully, By God, I'll be ready again—

"Eli, what's cortical stimulation?" she said, startling him, since he had been concentrating on another stimulation happening.

"Cortical stimulation . . . ?" he began, groping for words that wouldn't confound her.

"It's been mentioned so often today," she said.

It wasn't easy readjusting his thoughts, reversing that delicious anticipation settling down over him . . . He realized that during their months of marriage he rarely talked about his work with her, as he had done with Laura. Not that she wasn't intelligent or wouldn't understand. She just filled a different role in his life . . . they played well together, and it helped him to get away from his preoccupations . . . He told her now that it began mostly with a Canadian doctor, a neurologist named Wilder Penfield, who applied electrified probes to specific regions of the brain. "And these evoked long-forgotten memories so vividly that the subject felt he was actually reliving the experiences."

"Opening someone's head for that?" She had thrown a thin white cotton robe about herself.

"It was done during surgical procedures to relieve epileptic seizures," he explained, adding, "an intriguing by-product that he pursued because of its implications. And others, like myself—we went on from there. All in all it was quite a legacy he handed down."

"Apparently," she said, "considering this fuss."

Fuss. He reached over to the night table to light one of his long black cigarettes, which she disapproved of. He thought . . . all right, he was perhaps being rather dramatic . . . of Mrs. Isaac Newton referring to her husband's work as so much fuss over a falling apple, or Madame Einstein saying, "So the star twinkles red instead of blue, big fuss over *that?*" Overstating his case? . . . Well, sure, but when he considered the year-hours of painstaking work in the field since Penfield . . . by himself, others . . . the obstacles and contradictions that come with the territory of the human brain . . . He had been fortunate, he realized. More fortunate than so many others whose lives had been wasted in pursuit of the elusive *fata morgana.* He'd come to cortical stimulation late in his career. He already had his success—his reputation from his other research. This new, provocative work was a challenge—an enormous challenge for which he had put aside, had to put aside, ethics and even, to a degree, honesty. But it hurt. He was no casual, nor phony. Perhaps, in his fashion, he was a victim too . . .

These thoughts were in his mind as he described for Tessa the human brain, "that complex organ likened to a universe and packed with no fewer mysteries." Eli went on. "We push back the curtain of our ignorance just a bit, but then nature—as if begrudging us our intrusion—closes back the curtain, blocking us each step of the way. Yet we're tantalized by what we've learned and go on—"

"What is it *exactly* you're after?" she said.

He glanced sharply at her. He should have known the question was inevitable sooner or later. Hyperbole—obfuscating bullshit might work with others, but not with Tessa.

"It has to do," he said, quietly, "with the creation of . . . genius."

"Genius?" She became aware of a throbbing in her head, hoping she wasn't about to get one of those disabling migraines. Creating genius? It smacked of mad scientists, clashed with her own deep-rooted religious concepts. Vestiges of her Calvinist childhood.

"What do you call genius, Eli?" she asked. "You must have a special definition."

"Genius, he said, "is simply a talent for new discovery. The transforming of available information in a unique way. What evolves is seen as exciting, new and original."

"And this is—the program everyone speaks of?"

"Yes."

"Have you been"—she hesitated at the word—"successful?"

"Enough to feel encouraged," he replied. "Enough to continue on with it. One by one we lick the obstacles, are driven on, tantalized, mesmerized by the prospect of the breakthrough that over and over seems almost *there* . . ." With increasing excitement he went to talk about what the world could be with the emergence of, say, another Einstein, a da Vinci. "Your thing's music, darling. Consider another Beethoven. To produce them—"

"Produce? An odd word."

He laughed uneasily. "I didn't mean cloning, not anything like that."

"I didn't think you did."

"Tessa, out with it, what's bothering you?" He couldn't see her face. Her hair had fallen over it.

Her body was still. He was aware of the tension in it as she said, "You haven't been happy, Eli. Not even these last few days. These are days to be happy, aren't they?"

He had lit a cigarette. Reaching for the ashtray, he made the flicking off of the ash as delicate as one of his operations. Happy, he thought, trying to remember when he had last been entirely happy.

"I feel you're living with some sort of . . . pain."

"Nonsense."

"No, no, it's true, Eli. Even today when they were

saying all those beautifully extravagant things about you, I felt you weren't even listening."

Damn it, he thought, his privacy *was* a very special thing to him, especially the privacy of his thoughts. He didn't like intrusions into it, not even by this woman he loved—

"Would this cortical stimulation really make the world a better place?"

"I've no doubt of it."

"But would it be right?"

Ah, the old tampering-with-God business, that's what was bothering her. That religious streak in her.

"Right, wrong," he said, somewhat more at ease now. "When a scientist asks himself too many questions like that he risks the dangers of self-paralysis." He suddenly realized he was quoting verbatim Norville Kondorf at the Center, words he'd considered specious at the time . . .

"I'm not talking about that," she said. "Right, wrong —I know you'll decide that properly . . . I just wonder that what's bothering me hasn't bothered you."

"What's that?"

"The people you're dealing with," she said. "The people who honored you today—strewed flowers in your path. *Gloria in excelsis* had been trundled out with all stops open, even the rose garden bit. Eli, you don't trust them and neither do I. How often have we talked about it? I don't mean the people at the symposium but the people who arranged it all. Who engineered it. The others . . . maybe even the president himself—"

"Don't say these things," he said, feeling annoyed.

"But, Eli, darling—"

"I know, I know—"

"So this we agree on—"

"Nevertheless, I take their money. They support the program." His voice had become testy.

She realized he would have liked to end the conversation, but she persisted. "And what do they want from you for their money? There's surely a *quid pro quo*—"

"These same people funded polio vaccine. Their money goes to cancer research. I could go on."

She couldn't explain what was driving her on. She knew he was irritated. She only knew that she didn't want the part of him she loved best spoiled . . . "Would your list include the atom? Or is that all past, forgotten?"

"Risks—"

"Yes, risks."

It was precisely those questions—among others—that *had* been bedeviling him. How deeply did Einstein, Ferme and the others consider the alternatives? Would they conceivably have left the bomb undiscovered if it hadn't been a crisis time? For how long? DNA reconstituting was another more recent controversy. With risks, to be sure. But science moved ahead along its irresistible course. Well, didn't it? "The risks do include, as I believe it's called, a 'Frankenstein Factor.' "

"The scientist's nightmare, you mean? Screwing up? Producing a monster?"

For a moment he was startled . . . she'd come close—too close—to the truth. But he dismissed it as impossible. She couldn't possibly imagine where the program had led him. What they produced in the operating room. Everything about the Institute suggested such respectability, who could suspect what went on in that obscure, clandestine section? The mistakes . . . those so-called discards. And yet there was the *promise*, the *hope* of elusive success . . .

"Eli," she was now saying, "why don't you take a nap? I'll wake you in time. Sleep."

Sleep, he thought. When was the last time he had slept well? He stretched out. She dimmed the lights. Far below on Sixteenth Street N.W., the car tires hissed on

45

the streets wet with a soft rain that had begun to fall. She went to the window and looked down. Elias Nunn lay crouched on the bed, his knees drawn up in a foetal position. His eyes remained open, and the visions behind them were troubled. Very damn troubled.

CHAPTER FOUR

THE RELATIONSHIP couldn't have had a more unpromising beginning, and yet there was room for it to degenerate even further.

The bureaucratic phantom managing the bizarre enterprise had arranged adjacent seats in the first-class section of the 747 flight to San Diego.

She was the first to come aboard. Minutes passed, the section was filling, and still there was no sign of him. The vacant seat beside her mocked her. What if the sonofabitch didn't show? She felt terrified. Abandoned. Worse, betrayed. She was given assurance he'd come along, and it was never really meant. It was only to get her off their backs. Now I'm about to find myself in California in some asshole hospital surrounded by palms and some surgeon I don't know doing a number in my head . . . This was her vision of the future when at the very last moment she saw him enter the cabin. She picked up a magazine from the pocket in front of her and immersed herself in an article on communal hot-tub bathing, not looking up once as he tossed his hand luggage into the overhead compartment and wearily sank into the seat beside her. . . .

The hours before had been hectic for him. He felt himself caught up in some irresistible process. The monolithic machinery of government laughed at his efforts to disengage himself. Nothing he did seemed to mean anything. No one he contacted helped. Lawyers, politicians, newspeople—all displayed one excuse or another why they could do nothing. His persistence drew blank, grim stares. His anger more angry rejoinders, even threats and warnings. The entire affair was an exercise in futility, until finally he had no alternative but to surrender and hurry to make the flight west.

His curiosity, though, had grown with each failure, each setback. Among the unanswered questions, perhaps the largest, there was the riddle of Elias Nunn's involvement. What conceivable interest could that famous, distinguished scientist find in a run-of-the-mill tumor resection? And Washington. Where did Washington fit into this? The idea had occurred to him almost at the very first that he had somehow stumbled into a hush-hush program of some sort, but he'd dismissed this almost at once. Washington hanky-panky was past history, for the immediate future at least. Watergate and other more recent investigations had pretty much seen to that, he thought, with a naïve belief in his own political sophistication.

How little he knew. How ingenuous to believe that things truly changed, that government could operate on any other principle than that the end justified the means. One just had to be more careful; and as for that funny-putty called morality, professionals who performed the nitty-gritty still regarded it as a meretricious nuisance. The true criteria were results. Ultimate judgment was based on that. And rightly so . . .

He glanced at his watch. At this very moment he should have been halfway through a complicated spinal fusion. Clinic would have been at eleven, and after rounds his office hours. Later perhaps a consultation or two. He recalled with guilt feelings the difficulty of telling certain patients that someone besides himself would be taking care of them during his absence. Despite his assurances, there was suspicion, anger, and in one or two instances incipient hysteria as a result of anxiety and fear. In spite of his reputation for being hard-nosed, he was keenly aware of their emotional investment in him. He was, at least in his patients' opinion, that tenuous thread anchoring them to survival. To them, for the moment, he was godlike. How often had he felt entirely helpless before what he considered those delusions, yet how could he, in all mercy, deny them the comfort of faith?

"Goddamn you, Doctor Ephraim," he cursed silently as the plane's engines roared for takeoff. "You and your referrals." He was in the ambiguous position of being her physician of record, with all that implied, and at the same time feeling a bitter dislike. He tried to resolve it by considering himself the victim of a woman using her anxiety as a mask for self-indulgence. . . .

Luncheon was served in due course. Still no word—no acknowledgment of each other. Connie ate sparingly, toying with the seafood salad she had chosen. Her nourishment centered on a martini that she put away without apparent effect. Still no word, no sign between them. Not one single common courtesy that travelers occasionally exchange. The wall of hostility remained solid, unbreached.

One, two glasses of white wine was usually her quota, especially at lunch. Here she was lapping up martinis and she wondered why. Had she expected him to reach out, stop her with an "Enough of that now"? Well, wasn't that his job? He seemed oblivious of her as he ate his way through a double helping of sirloin tips. She wanted to tell him he looked ridiculous, a grown man feeding himself with tiny plastic utensils more appropriate for child's play . . . She noted his heavy hands and thick fingers, which somehow moved with a certain grace and efficient economy. She saw those same fingers and hands pulling the insides of her head apart.

She felt a surge of anger. Goddamn it, she thought, what was with this cold indifference? So he had been sandbagged. Hijacked. He was still her doctor, wasn't he?

The pilot, for reasons known only to himself, announced they were over Gary, Indiana, which left most of the passengers visibly unimpressed. She had been staring out the window, sorting out her feelings. Wisps of nasty gray clouds raced by like scurrying ghosts. There were glimpses of farmlands reaching endlessly to the horizon. Spring runoffs spilled over river banks, spoiling the neat patterns of the farms. She felt unaccountably saddened by the sight as she realized that what seemed so placid and serene from this height was probably wet hell down there. Could the same deception be true of her? What she seemed to be, and what she was? A victory of style over substance? The passengers aboard—the flight attendants even—they probably saw her as a chic broad off on some glamorous jaunt. A fling on the islands. Meeting a boyfriend in films, records or some such. Off to Malibu. Newport. What would they think if they knew she was en route for brain surgery? They'd be annoyed probably. Disturbed for a brief moment. They'd made a small miscalculation. Ah, well, screw you, ladies and gentlemen . . .

The first martini had been gulped quickly. She rang for the stewardess. "I'd like—" There it was again! That loss for words. Knowing what she wanted to say without being able to say it. That feeling of helplessness. Frustration. The Shadow was up to his merry pranks again. Helplessly, she held her glass out.

"The lady'd like another martini, I believe," Phil Carlino volunteered. He didn't even turn to acknowledge her cold look. He had been involved in a paperback he had picked up in his rush through the terminal. It turned out to be a purple-passaged romantic novel of the times of Louis the Sixteenth. He had been transported into a world of heaving bosoms and tossed-up petticoats in the rampant passions of the period. He had settled back, even slipped off his loafers. His feet were tired from the rushing about during the past several hours. He of course knew she was there, sitting beside him, but he wasn't prepared to handle a confrontation yet, saying what he would like to have said—

"How long will it take for my hair to grow back?" she asked, her voice as casual as she could make it. Well, one had to say *something* . . .

Carefully he dog-eared the page he had been reading. The question didn't surprise him. Stressed patients exhibited bizarre priorities, he knew.

"I've brought along one or two wigs," she went on, "but a wig's one thing when you have your hair. Your own hair, you know?"

He was looking steadily into her eyes now. "How do you see me?" he asked.

"What do you mean?"

"My role. My position, I mean. I'm not your doctor any longer."

"I didn't know that," she said truthfully.

"What did you expect? Have you any idea what I've been put through—?"

"Because of me."

"Because of you, yes."

"What do I do?" she heard herself say.

"I don't know what button you pushed, but let me go," he said. "As for what you do, it's your business, yours entirely."

Turning about to the glass rectangle of window, her thoughts streaked by rapidly as the cloud wisps outside, thoughts as bleakly gray. "Another thing," she heard him say, "I don't know what it is you expect of me."

There it was . . . the very same question she had been asking of herself. What exactly *did* she want of him? When he first visited her in her hospital room she remembered feeling good. She came to look forward to his visits, to depend on them, in fact. She'd glance at her watch, repeatedly ask the nurse if Doctor Carlino was on the floor. Once or twice she asked herself what was going on. What was happening? Was it he himself or his physician role? She settled for the fact of her loneliness, her abandonment by family, the entire damn human race except for a few preoccupied friends who deep down wouldn't care less if she fell off, the end of the earth . . .

She recalled once meeting an attractive man at a Bridgehampton party. He said he was a Corinthian and went on to explain what it meant. He hung out about marinas and fancy yachts of all classes. The wealthy owners would invite him along for cruises, since he knew about the sea—how to fix an engine, reef a sail, also how to "amuse the ladies." He was neither a member of the crew nor one of the guests, but something in between. He was simply a gentleman sailor named after that hard-shelled mollusk which attaches itself to the hull of vessels, traveling the world with no will of its own. And no effort. Was she a Corinthian too, she wondered. Attaching herself to passing gentlemen and, in the words of the famous playwright, depending upon "the kindness of strangers"?

52

"I didn't want to go alone," she said. There, she thought. She'd said it, and it was the truth. "And you were it," she continued, "since it was agreed you're my doctor." She glanced down to his lap. His eyes followed. The paperback rested there, cover up. It was a boudoir scene of the period, a fourposter in the background, with the seduction of a bewigged, wide-eyed beauty imminent. Their eyes lifted. Met. Surprise must have shown in hers.

"What did you expect?" he muttered. *"Cragg's Applied Neurochemistry?"*

It was the amusement behind his dark eyes that broke the ice. He was human after all, she thought. It was certainly the first indication of it since they had met. "To answer your question," she said. "Doctor Ephraim, I believe, handed me over to you. Doesn't that make you my doctor?"

"Doctor Nunn will be your doctor," he replied. "And if his eminence is true to type, I'll cease to exist."

"Would he mind if you held my hand?" Even as she said it, she regretted it. She saw the black eyes go bleak and she knew what he was thinking . . . the hell she had raised in his life to comfort some hysterical broad. She thought of adding, "How would you word it on my bill?" Instead, she said, "What will he do—this Doctor Nunn? What would you have done?"

He would do at least that much for her. In terms she could understand, he explained how a hole the size of a silver dollar would be trepanned in that protective bone covering called the skull. He described the human brain as a mass of tissue, pinkish gray on the outside, white in its inner recesses, weighing about fifteen hundred grams. On the back of a magazine he took from the pocket of the seat in front of him he drew a crude picture of the walnut-shaped organ.

As he spoke, he seemed to forget whatever negative

feelings he had toward her. Leaning closer to him, she hung on each word, each explanation. Trying to apply what he said to her own brain and its condition. It was as if comprehending the details of her ailment—that unspeakable thing—it would somehow vanish. Come out, come out, wherever you are. I know you . . .

He described the brain's cortex and its various lobes —the occipital, temporal and frontal. The midbrain with its medulla and cerebellum. He delineated the divisions, those hemispheres which handled the body's activities and sensory functions. Pointing to an area in the frontal lobe, he explained it as the region where speech, memory and other functions were handled.

"Handled," she murmured.

"Yes."

Cool bastard, she thought.

"An understatement," he admitted, going on to explain that wondrous and still partially unknown process by which messages are received and transmitted to the brain which in turn stimulate the appropriate responses. For a moment he forgot himself. He was at the lectern explaining to a group of first-year interns the chemistry and biophysics of transmitter substances. He even slipped into a vernacular she couldn't possibly comprehend.

"Hey, *hey,*" she said softly, smiling. "It's me."

He laughed.

He actually laughed, she thought, and then said, "Where did we leave my shadow?"

"We go in through a slot we make here."

"A slot," she murmured wryly. "Drop a quarter in, get lemons."

He glanced sharply at her . . . in a flash she'd showed him her terror masked by flippancy. Better than most, he thought, recognizing it as a form of courage . . . "I'll be there," he heard himself say.

"Yes," she said softly, a note of humility there for the first time (and which didn't escape him). "Thank you." Over Sioux Falls, the thaw was almost total.

Other than her talents in bed, Connie was adept in a deceptively simple art, one of the tools of her trade. Listening. To listen unobtrusively. To ask just the right questions, bringing out further confidences. Pleasing. And not even the hard, tough shell of Phil Carlino could resist her genuine interest. Or her genuine vulnerability.

"My father wanted me to join the police force the way my brother did," he was saying now, telling her about his youth.

"Angie," she murmured.

He nodded. "He's a plainclothes detective attached to homicide. He lives in Pelham. Has a wife, three kids and an almost paid up hot-tub."

"Tell me about your mother. She sounds unusual."

A warm look came into his eyes, softening them. "She is," he said, and went on to describe how she had fought off his father's wishes during that crucial time of deciding which way he'd go. "Tradition. We're great for tradition," he said. "Pop had half his spleen shot away by some punk in an alley and now life's playing bocci. Chasing a little ball with a bigger one. Who do you suppose runs an Italian family? The old man? Don't believe it. That's all macho face-saving. Mine's no different. Tough as my pop is, when it comes to the big decisions, she gets her way. My mother, I mean." He explained how she had manipulated his father, having Don Julio, the priest of her church, not only intercede but get him enrolled at Fordham. "After that—" His large hands gestured that from there on his life took on its own momentum.

She felt she understood Phil Carlino almost better than she understood herself. Why he went the way he did. Odd, she thought. How perceptive—what insights one could have about others and fuck up with yourself.

She saw him as a young man caught between two parents, each with his own needs. Reaching out for a sort of extension of themselves. Connie couldn't guess why the woman wanted her son to be a doctor. A Jewish mother was one thing. An Italian . . . maybe the needs were universal . . . that assertive reach for respect. Success. Interchangeable, and synonymous. That special word with special meanings—*respeto.* The class lines and the eternal hunger to break through. If not by themselves, by their children. She understood his obsession with work. It was his repayment of the debt he'd run up for his parents' sacrifice. For the determination of an indomitable mother. It also helped her further understand his resentment of her behavior. . . .

Flying over the Grand Canyon, as the pilot announced, she said, "Ask me why I'm a hooker." It was said with a motive. Let him have a few points in repayment. Some moral superiority.

He didn't rise to it, though. He merely shook his head indifferently. "I get it all the time, y'know," she went on. " 'A *nice* . . . a pretty girl like you.' Aren't you curious?"

"Not particularly," he said, wondering why he was annoyed. He had become aware of certain new, disquieting feelings toward her. For instance—why should he be speculating on what it would be like making love to her?

"I couldn't tell you anyway," she was saying. "Not exactly."

A few short hours ago he could have kicked her ass. Now he was thinking on better, more pleasurable uses for it. Goddamn it, you idiot . . . watch out . . .

"Natalie Burnham's my name." The young woman in the attractive pants suit introduced herself the moment they disembarked. Her figure was slight, her features not unattractive. Black hair tightly drawn back into a bun gave her a prim quality, but her smile was warm and friendly. "I'm from the Institute," she pertly announced. She requested their baggage stubs. "Arthur will get your bags." She asked that they follow her.

The limousine was close by, almost on the tarmac. Phil was impressed. It reminded him of the time he had been whisked off to Kuwait on a Lear jet sent for him. He was to attend the ailing newphew of a sheik. Here was the same heavy, privileged treatment.

Arthur, the chauffeur, somehow bothered Phil. He drove the freeway with professional skill. His twill uniform fitted him perfectly and his manner was correct; and yet—Phil couldn't precisely put his finger on it. As he himself might have said, "You don't spend a lifetime living with two police officers without recognizing another."

Their guide chattered ceaselessly, to their annoyance. Neither Connie nor Phil had any interest in restored Spanish missions, coastal nuclear plants, nor even intrepid young people hurling themselves over a high cliff aboard glorified kites.

Connie had to shake the feeling she was a tourist.

As for Phil, he felt a certain excitement of anticipation. The mystery would shortly be resolved, the unanswered riddle answered. He interrupted a discourse on more local geography to inquire, "How soon do I meet Doctor Nunn?"

A sudden stillness in the car. A tension. Their escort's chatter shut off like a broken tape. Her expression went icily void. Phil, looking up, caught the chauffeur eyeing him through the rear-view mirror, and what he saw in those eyes didn't exactly please him.

"Doctor Nunn is out of town," was the quiet, studied reply from their escort. "You'll hear from Doctor Kondorf."

"Doctor Kondorf?"

"Our director."

Connie wasn't unaware of the hostility directed toward Phil, and it didn't help reassure her about her own situation. It didn't sit well with her that her personal physician was *persona non grata*.

Her apprehensions, though, were soon dispelled as the limousine glided off the freeway to take a secondary road. A short while later it slowed in front of two red-brick gateposts on which were mounted cement vases of multicolored geraniums. The car turned into a white graveled driveway. Several hundred yards further, passing through a well-manicured wooded terrace, an enchanting spectacle greeted them . . . a large gingerbread structure of the turn of the century; wide wooden verandas girded the well-preserved structure of cupolas and gables and wooden fretwork. The car stopped underneath a porte cochere guarding the entrance.

"What's this?" Connie said, turning to Natalie Burnham. For a moment she thought she was at a sanitarium for the wealthy aged.

"The Sorrento Inn." Their guide smiled. "You'll stay here tonight," and turning to Phil, "Doctor Kondorf will phone you. You have Miss Keenan's charts and records?"

The Sorrento Inn had a long tradition. It was a large wooden structure of Edwardian design. A maze of mansards and gables, magnificently maintained and everything painted fresh. It was a unique anachronism which attracted a nostalgic clientele and those who wished to escape the Howard Johnsons or Holiday Inns. Eight Presidents, a Prince of Wales and Galli-Curci had slept and dined here and one would not have been surprised to encounter their ghosts at night on one of the dark, polished wood staircases. The grounds were no less impressive with their enormous box hedges and trees and landscaping, which would have shamed a baronial park. . . .

Their suites adjoined each other, and flowers and fruit had been thoughtfully provided. Connie, regarding the magnificent four-poster bed, could only murmur, "Jesus!"

"I'm sure you'll be comfortable." Ms. Burnham smiled.

Disneyland, was all Connie could think of as she looked about, wide-eyed. A bellboy of at least sixty, in proper uniform, wheeled in their bags. Natalie Burnham gave him his instructions about which bag went where, then left.

For several moments Connie stood in the center of her sitting room curiously regarding antimacassars, haircloth and needlepoint upholstery—even a shelf of books in gilt-tooled Moroccan bindings. There was a knock on the door, which opened into Phil's own suite. As she opened it he said, "Ready for the waters?"

They both laughed. "A high colonic with irradiated Perrier," she said, adding, "Your Doctor Nunn may really be on to something. I bet my vapors will just vanish."

CHAPTER FIVE

LEAVING TESSA sleeping, Eli, although weary himself from the trip, showered and dressed and, after gulping a handful of vitamins along with a glass of juice, impatiently took off for the Center. Rosarita, the housekeeper, arrived as he was leaving, and her greeting was warm yet properly respectful in her dignified *compesino* manner.

Descending the steep winding road, the '72 Volvo made unpleasant popping noises. Eli was a perfectionist. Anything or anyone about him was required to perform in perfect order; today, however, the engine's dysfunction went unnoticed. . . .

The Jenifer Frumkin Institute for Physiological Studies had once been part of a vast Mexican ranch reaching up almost to the next county. What had once been the hacienda with old adobe structures with red-tiled roofs was now a complex of modern white concrete, glass and stainless steel nestled in amid rolling hills overlooking the Pacific. Meandering landscaped walks and even a sculpture garden dominated by a huge Henry Moore gave it the appearance of a well-endowed university campus, this impression enhanced by the traffic of young people, some in white tunics and jackets, and among these some with stethoscopes just happening to snake from their pockets.

The tallest of the structures was the general clinic, a teaching hospital where excellence was the criteria among staff and interns. Its reputation was such that patients from all over the world sought treatment here where the most advanced medicine was practiced and researched.

Jenifer Frumkin herself had been a spinster millionairess whose fortune was identified with a patent medicine for female disorders. At her death her fortune was bequeathed to found the Institute, a highly worthy cause to be sure; and incidentally, an ideal cover to house the Elias Nunn Institute of Behavioral Research funded by the government and various cooperating corporations. The Center was kept separate and apart from the Institute's other activities and was located in a remote section of the complex. Except for those who had business there, it was considered just another research facility among several.

It was a special place even physically, with its double-fenced compound of squat businesslike buildings. The sole entrance was past a well-guarded sentry house where anyone who did enter was thoroughly checked out.

Approaching the Institute's grounds, Eli noted that the day's traffic had already begun. Although aware that the entire Institute was merely a lightning rod to divert attention away from the Center and its secret activity, he now felt that at least some compensating good came of it.

The uniformed guard at the sentry house saluted

smartly as he drove through. Parking his car in its allotted space, he hurried into the larger of the buildings. Taking the stairs two at a time, he came to the upper floor, where he strode to the nurses' station.

The chart-rack only held two metal-bound charts. For several minutes he anxiously reviewed the data he found there, and what he saw didn't please him.

A middle-aged, competent-looking nurse had been regarding him. Now she slowly approached. Glancing up, he murmured, "Not much change."

"No, sir." She pushed back a wisp of reddish hair beneath the starched cap.

"Floyd's hyperactivity's—"

"The same. He's not only driving himself too hard, he's driving everyone else crazy."

"Thorazine was prescribed, I see. By whom?"

"Doctor Jelke," she said. "It slowed him some. You'll notice he carries on now sometimes without the electric pulse."

He nodded. "Any sleep?"

"Sleep? Neither of them sleeps."

He nodded as he thoughtfully replaced the charts, making a sharp noise in the quiet of the entire floor. As he left the station, Nurse Mary Chatterton asked if he needed her to come along.

"No."

The vinyled corridor, austere and septic as any hospital, had a series of identical heavy doors. Entering one which slid open noiselessly, he found himself in a small foyer with another heavy door directly ahead. To the right was a flight of three steps with a glassed door leading to what appeared to be a control booth filled with sophisticated monitoring equipment. These provided data on the immediate condition of the subject below, in a room separated by a one-way window.

Eli nodded a greeting to the young technician sitting

at the console. For a moment he gazed through the window, studying the subject. The almost bare room of stark white, even ceiling and floor, created the surrealistic effect of everything within floating in space. Eli turned to consult the monitors, giving attention to vital signs, especially the brain's electrical activity. For several moments he watched as the paper tape moved beneath the quivering styli. Shaking his head he commented more to himself than to the technician, "No change."

"No, sir."

Tillie Harper, a spinster in her mid-forties, had once been a librarian in a small town near Lenox, Massachusetts. Now gaunt and fragile-looking, her fine features suggested a patrician heritage. The color of her natural hair was indeterminate since she now wore a dark, unattractive wig, slightly askew. A flower-patterned housedress sizes too large enhanced her gauntness. Her feet were in felt slippers and her bare legs were pale and terribly thin.

She stood motionless, facing the two walls at their junction, staring down at her feet, not seeing them. She seemed almost more effigy than human being. Eli said gently, "Tillie . . . Tillie, would you turn around?"

Nothing.

"This is Doctor Nunn, Tillie. I've come to see how you are."

She might have been carved from stone.

He returned slowly to the control booth, where he instructed the technician to transmit twenty-five microvolts for a two-second duration. Adjusting the rheostats, the technician looked up to Eli.

He nodded. A small toggle switch was thrown. Both men saw the woman below shudder ever so slightly as by shortwave radio she received the charge through two terminals implanted in her skull.

Eli reached over, throwing open the intercom. "Tillie," he said, "can you hear me?"

As before, there was no response. Tillie Harper had always been alone in her life, rarely communicating. When she disappeared from her hometown she was no more noticed than the cold season's fallen leaves. Her kind of life, or nonlife, was one of the desired criteria for Eli Nunn's subjects. At least if something happened few would be left to mourn. Or so, in part, the rationalization went. It helped, though often not enough, to assuage conscience. Tillie Harper, a woman alone, was never more that . . . apparently . . . than at this moment . . .

Returning to the EEG with its running tape, Eli noted the slight spiking of the transmission after which it returned to its familiar abnormal pattern.

Floyd Gibbs, subject number two, was Tillie Harper's neighbor. His was an entirely different situation. His room was a scene of frenetic activity as technicians struggled to keep up with a torrent of material of a very special nature. Although both Tillie and Floyd were subjects of the same procedure, the effects of it on them were dramatically different. Tillie had been left an apparent vegetable, whereas the other became what could only be described as hyperactive.

A massive black man, Floyd Gibbs once had been a puddler in a Youngstown, Ohio, steel mill. With an IQ between ninety and one hundred, as a boy he had been allowed to graduate from public school in Covington, Kentucky. That had been the sum total of his formal education except for some feeble efforts in various penitentiaries to teach him a trade.

A huge block pulley had swung against Floyd's skull, crushing it. The surgeons in Youngstown despaired of repairing the massive damage. The hospital computer meanwhile had passed on certain data, so that in a very short while Floyd Gibbs was en route to California by special plane.

Elias Nunn undertook the repair of the damaged brain, and succeeded to the minimal extent that the man would survive; however, instead of closing-up for the usual convalescence, Nunn went on to the procedure involving the electric probe, the purpose of which was to stimulate cortical tissue for whatever would evolve.

The success was as unforeseen as it was phenomenal. Floyd Gibbs, barely above the level of simple-mindedness, became from one moment to the next a genius in the special field of higher mathematics known as Catastrophe Theory. In every other respect, though, he also became exactly as Tillie Harper. . . .

Catastrophe Theory was a newly discovered, arcane concept with a practical application. The modality, through complex formulae and graphing, offered a solution to certain problems such as the precise wavelength at which the color blue becomes green . . . when exactly a child is no longer a child but a grownup . . . do cows think? . . . the precise moment day becomes night . . . The possibilities of describing matter became unlimited, and in a manner hitherto unknown. . . .

Floyd Gibbs, of course, had never heard of Catastrophe Theory, yet here he was now its master, an unqualified genius as the result of Elias Nunn brushing certain brain cells with his electric probe.

Both the activity in the control room as well as in the room below were far different than in his neighbor's. Technicians busily recorded both on video and sound tape all that went on. Floyd Gibbs himself, stripped to the waist and sweating profusely from his exertions, could hardly keep up with his own brain's special activity. On large sheets of paper he dashed off complex formulations and sweeping graph lines. A team of technicians saw to it that his busy hands never lacked for writing materials. As one page filled, it was swept away and replaced by another. The product of the unique mind was immediately rushed to analysts, who translated it for the computer.

Why had Floyd Gibbs become a candidate for the "procedure"? Why Tillie Harper? And more recently Connie Keenan? All had several things in common according to criteria established by the top-secret committee in Washington. All had some brain dysfunction and were scheduled for surgery. All were considered in otherwise good physical condition; and all had a chance of surviving the operation.

Very important among the major criteria was that all were loners, living a solitary life with no one dependent upon them, and also no one interested enough to make inquiries into their disappearance. . . .

Eli, leaning forward, could see the voltmeter's thin needle wavering and knew that the man in the room below was receiving the brain stimulation necessary to keep him in a creative frenzy. A man possessed, he peered into a world of symbols and numbers marching in strange configurations. Everything else was nonexistent for Floyd Gibbs and apparently always would be. Catastrophe Theory had taken over his life—itself a catastrophe . . . ?

The technician at the console watched intently as the sweep hand of the chronograph came to a critical point. His finger pressed the toggle switch cutting off the transmission. Eli could see the man below go instantaneously rigid. All movement—life—seemed interrupted. Great wide eyes stared, apparently seeing nothing. His torso glistened from his previous exertions. Two aides assisted him gently to a plain wooden chair. He sat stiffly, slowly, like a very old man. Someone thoughtfully rubbed his body down with a white towel, as if he were a thoroughbred after an exercise sprint.

The console technician turned to Eli. *"Incredible,"* he said, shaking his head. "Simply *incredible . . ."*

Eli stared at the man. He could say nothing. He realized that Floyd Gibbs was somehow considered almost a total success. Almost. Justification certainly for their continuing dedication to the program. He could only think of saying, "Does he ask for food?"

The young man regarded Eli oddly. "No, sir."

"Does he say anything?"

A headshake.

"To go to the toilet?"

Negative.

"Not one single word?" His voice was rising. It was, almost, a plea. Eli realized he was alone in his feelings about what had been done to two people. The number of individuals privy to the nature of the "program" was kept for security reasons to a minimum. Few knew that it was an entirely separate procedure, unrelated to the specific medical welfare of the patient. Yet those on his staff who did know had a strange callousness. Maybe it was protective coloration. Or maybe somewhere along the way they had lost sight of the fact—forced themselves to lose sight of it, perhaps—that the subjects were people. Human beings like themselves. All were good, honest people, Eli had no doubt of that. Well, the chief surgeon in an operating room was the captain of a ship. All responsibility was his. This would make it easier for the others, to be sure—but what of himself?

Doctor Norville Kondorf, director of the Jenifer Frumkin Institute, was fortunate in that he realized early enough in his career that the practice of medicine wasn't his forte. This revelation came to him while he was interning at a Maryland hospital. He was doubly fortunate in that shortly thereafter he realized his true strength: he was an executive at heart. He could deal with people, manipulate them with a facile, Byzantine deviousness. It was almost inevitable that he should turn to hospital administration.

When the Committee of Bio-Energetic Affairs had to decide who should administer the Institute, the matter had been turned over to the computer. Norville Kondorf emerged as first choice.

In his forties now, he was as impeccable in the management of the facility as he was about himself. Everything about him was trim, sleekly handsome. He was a top-seeded tennis player at the local club; his tailoring strictly Rodeo Drive, as was his hair styling. He was a Vitamin E addict and had a Procaine prescription filled in Tijuana. He could be found every morning at seven, weather permitting, jogging along the beach. . . .

"Doctor Nunn is here," his secretary was saying now over the intercom.

Four pharmaceutical detail men and two Institute bureau heads looked up from their *JAM* or *Sports Illustrated* to regard the famous man who had just strode into the reception room on his way to the director's office. The deep-set eyes and set of the jaw were enough to deflect any casual greeting or idle remark. Eli's air suggested he was not about to suffer gladly either fools or intruders into his privacy.

"Go right in, sir," the secretary said, unnecessarily, since he was on his way there.

Opening the door to Kondorf's office, Eli almost stumbled into a woman who was leaving. Chief of an immunological service, she gave him an angry look . . . it had taken days for an appointment with the director to discuss important matters; now she had been hustled out.

69

"Eli. Eli, my God, it's good to *see* you." Norville Kondorf swept from behind his neat glass-topped desk, hands outstretched, his tanned face in smiles. "Don't tell me!" he said. "I know all about it . . . a triumph . . . a real triumph . . ." And now for a bit of humor . . . "Where's the laurel wreath—?"

"Sit down, Norville," Eli said, thinking the man was forever into one role or another. Indeed, he turned them on as though they were spigots. An old-fashioned soda fountain came to his mind . . . a bit of charm here, no cherry, please. Some sympathy . . . get tough now . . .

The director, instead of returning behind his desk, chose a suede, doe-colored Barcelona chair, inviting Eli to take the other. He went on to explain everything had been covered during his absence. "I myself made rounds with Dick Jelke once or twice."

It was the opening Eli wanted. "Then you've seen our two subjects," he said. The intercom on the desk buzzed. "Please shut that damned thing off."

Kondorf quietly told his secretary he wasn't to be disturbed. Looking up, he saw Eli glowering at him. Ah, he thought, here we go again . . .

Norville Kondorf had been selected by Washington to administer the Institute as a whole; however, the managing of the Center was his primary responsibility. The hiring and firing of personnel, the host of administrative details, could have been handled by any number of applicants, perhaps even better than himself, but none could handle Elias Nunn as well. And for that reason alone he had been selected. To keep the maverick genius, the *enfant terrible* in line, out of embarrassing situations and his doubts and conscience pangs suppressed. Nothing, absolutely nothing could be permitted to interfere with the program's progress and ultimate success . . .

"As for our subjects," Kondorf said, replying to Eli's

question, "you yourself said time could change their condition—"

"So I did, but I was only voicing a hope, not a belief."

Kondorf shook his head ruefully. Experience had taught him never to meet the scientist head on. "You enjoyed the trip, Eli? You and your lady?"

"It was useful."

Kondorf nodded. "You understand our nation's gratitude."

"I meant I had the opportunity to stand off from myself and think some on what I've done—"

"You and your reflections. Those perennially gloomy reflections . . . typical, of course, of the perfectionist you are. Eli . . . you expect the worst, and come away achieving the best."

Eli lit one of his black cigarettes. "Have I achieved the best?"

Here it comes, Kondorf thought.

"What's even good about it? It's bad, worse . . . may God forgive me . . ."

Oh, hell, Kondorf thought. Now we've got God on our hands. What he said was, "We have to see the program from the larger perspective. You mention God. Well, surely God understands the ultimate good we mean to achieve." And he went on to quote what he was certain Elias Nunn already knew: the words of Carl Rogers, who said that the social power of the human brain could make atomic energy feeble by comparison. Next he invoked Skinner, who justified silence in its efforts to control human behavior. As he spoke he tried to evaluate Eli's depression. On a scale of one to ten, he settled for a seven. Perhaps an eight even. Depending . . .

Eli was now countering that Penfield himself had said something to the effect that science throws no light on the nature of the spirit of man or God . . .

"Well, be that as it may, I needn't tell you, Eli, that the

history of research is a story of disappointments and failures. The point is, the objective needs to be viewed with a tunnel vision."

Both men were now standing at the large picture window, side by side, looking out over the Institute grounds. At the farthest end was the Center, and beyond that the ocean, glistening in the sun.

But Eli was seeing nothing of this. He was peering inward, into some morbidly gloomy recess of his mind, where tormented images were trying to escape the confrontation with his guilts . . . By now he was on intimate terms with his self-styled character flaw, acknowledging its existence secretly. He was a "right person." He had this *need* to be right not only to everyone else, but most importantly—to himself. Sometimes it required him to dissemble, rearrange facts, which he handled with characteristic flair. He could find convincing rationales, reasons proving his rightness; and of course there was his formidable reputation, which never made it easy to question him. His fantasies projected into universal truths . . . Am I a spoiled child?, he often asked himself, and would answer, If I am, I'm at least one in a good cause. An egoist? Yes, he conceded that readily and believed with good reason that his achievements mostly justified his egoism. His sincerity, especially in his social positions, was unequivocal.

And he was honest enough to realize that his remarkable success was surely from the energy that came from his egoism. In his work, he pursued his beliefs and theories with a relentless determination. He was *compelled* to do it to prove himself right. To himself. To the world. His motivations? Not altogether noble, he realized, but in the process he was advancing knowledge. He was treating, healing people . . . When he'd stood on the dais receiving the Nobel Prize, he had even dared to think of himself as one of a brotherhood of "right people" including Galileo, Newton, and others whose complicated motives and characters had been kindly blurred by time . . .

Norville Kondorf knew the game he was expected to play out. Eli would say, I quit, and he would pretend to be shocked, say, "Oh, no, you mustn't," and offer intellectually appealing rationales.

Eli was now saying, "Can any physiologist repeat an experiment precisely? We're not lab people, chemists working under controlled conditions who'd be happy if the scatter on their results hit an average of twenty percent. How acceptable would such a tolerance be to a neurosurgeon?"

"It wouldn't be," the director agreed.

Eli went on to say that he could place an electrode in the brain within half a millimeter of its target. "But so what? Even if my aim is as perfect as the state of the art permits, do I know which cells will respond? Which won't? What if it struck off-center? What if the probe is somehow faulty? And what about anomalies? Dead or dying cells? What consistency is there in the human brain? What exactness? Can a precise paradigm be charted? Data from one cell group proves good. From another—nothing. Two brains anywhere in the world with exactly the same cell arrangement of axons and dendrites are a mathematical impossibility. Norville, the operating table isn't a research lab. We're not dealing with frogs and cuttlefish. These are people, and my probe is an insult."

The room was still for several moments. Somewhere in the distance there was the scream of sea birds. A telephone rang in a distant room.

"People," Kondorf said quietly.

"Yes."

"Let's consider them for a moment, Eli. People, the human race. Are people supermen? Do we live forever?

We've made progress in medicine, sure, but mostly in preventative medicine. As for cures—therapy—we've a long way to go. Let me put a hypothetical question to you, my friend. What if one morning Elias Nunn tries the procedure on someone . . . someone of questionable social value . . . someone with a potentially fatal clot in the brain? Some other possible fatal injury? The prognosis is grim. But then, somehow, accident or not, Eli Nunn touches with his electrified probe a particular brain cell. And what happens? Apparent miracle of miracles . . . the patient awakens and to everyone's surprise presents us with the answer to—let's say cancer. Perhaps all disease processes. Perhaps to the riddle of life itself. What about this, Eli? Couldn't the program do this for *people?*"

The man was in form today. He was playing the game well. Eli knew Norville's role was to keep him on a leash, yank on it when his doubts got too strong. He was there to siphon off the guilt, grounding any excessive buildup in self-recrimination. "You set the Washington trip up as an ego-massage," Eli said accusingly.

To lie would be the worst tactic, Kondorf realized. "In a good cause," he conceded.

Eli nodded. The man was hanging in there, he thought. "Good cause? I seem to recall hearing them talk about good causes . . . conquering disease . . . wiping out hunger, poverty . . . good causes, indeed, Norville. Except I sensed something else again, something that suggested laser-beam weaponry. Space warfare. Our other partners in our enterprise, the multinationals, they're thinking about politics and profits . . . Norville, you're a physician. You remember what they taught you at medical school?"

"I'm not sure what you mean—"

"Ethics—the minimal principle of our profession is to do no harm."

Again a brief silence. Eli realized he was making it hard for the man, but it was hard for him too. Harder. He pushed on. "Has the Federal Ethics Advisory Board evaluated us? Has our project even been put to them?"

"I wouldn't worry about that."

"They know nothing about us?"

"I said you shouldn't worry. Can't that be sufficient?" Kondorf disliked the role of victim, and damn it, the fellow was whipsawing him, playing an intellectual ping-pong game. Now you're in my court. Smash. Handle that, oldtimer. He was getting damn irritated. But he knew you didn't score if you lost control. He moved across the room and picked up a large amethyst paperweight from his desk. In the morning light, purple fire danced in his hand. "I suggest that your point of view is a little distorted, Eli—"

"Oh?"

"You're maybe too much influenced by your pretty young wife?" Kondorf realized he was on dangerous ground here, but he had to risk it. What's more, it was something he genuinely believed. He realized Eli was looking at him with surprised shock, but he had to follow through . . . He said that the last generation's anti-war demonstrators had become this generation's conservationists "who see God as a granola-eating backpacker. Certainly you've your own convictions. You're famous, if not notorious, for them. Still, I sense her touch in this, playing on you, your decency . . . Eli, forgive me, but I feel I really must say this. Resent it if you like, but it's my duty. You are not her property, Eli—"

"No?" Eli's look was dangerous.

"Nor your own, even."

"Oh?"

"You belong to *people*, Eli. You have, in a fashion, been called. I mean it. You have been called, and you are a sort of national resource, you should be beyond conventional guilts and moral issues. I mean, they're out of *context*, can't you see that . . . ?"

In spite of himself, part of Eli was really not displeased by this recital. Damn it, he wished it weren't so, but how to deny that warm feeling in his gut . . . ?

At this moment the administrator's secretary came in with a tray of coffee things. Both men watched in intense silence, almost as if they had never seen such an amazing thing before, as she poured and handed each a mug of coffee as she knew he liked it—Eli's without sugar and a bit of cream, Kondorf's black. In a moment she was gone and both men silently sipped at the hot brew.

Eli wasn't through. He wasn't doing this out of cruelty or intellectual curiosity, he told himself. His waffling was not put on. He was a man hung up on some very sharp points of a moral dilemma, and he badly needed help to free himself. "As program chief I consider the program has failed—"

"*Failed?*"

"You made rounds, you saw the results."

Back to square one, Kondorf thought.

"Catatonia seems inevitable," Eli was saying. "We're fighting an incontrovertible law of nature that sustains —even demands—equilibrium. Take from one side of the equation, you must give to the other. That's what we've accomplished, Norville. A grim trade-off. We've tampered with an immutable, universal law. Without it, it all comes apart."

For a moment Kondorf said nothing, stood there staring at Eli. Then he turned and crossed to his desk. From a drawer he extracted a folder that he brought to Eli. "Read it, please."

When the director saw Eli had no intention of taking it, he recited its contents.

"These are complaints from the computer people and the analysts who are handling Floyd Gibbs material."

Kondorf went on to point out that the staff was unable to maintain Gibbs' pace of output. "And the quality of the material is no less astonishing. We still haven't realized the full impact of it."

"And Tillie Harper?"

"Floyd Gibbs justifies Tillie Harper," the director almost shouted. "A dozen—two dozen Tillie Harpers—"

Eli shook his head.

Kondorf's tone became careful, studied. He was wearying of the exercise and yet he knew he was approaching the crucial moment. "Eli," he said, "I'm sure you're familiar with Clark's Law. You might have coined it yourself. 'The next great scientific advance will be the one the most eminent scientist has most recently called impossible.' " He came toward Eli, who was slouched down in the chair, considering his folded hands. "You've created something very special, a superior being out of a very common one . . . and it pains me—truly it does— to hear you denigrating yourself as well as your achievement. You call it failure, I would call it success. A damn brilliant success. One out of two, it's true. But we've hardly begun. My God, Eli, your very next attempt could be the breakthrough. Imagine it . . . a technique, a modality to create genius almost to order. The personal tragedies that upset you—and, of course, rightly—will have been eliminated. You'll have created an entire new order of superior people . . . think of it, Eli, think of just *that*, and nothing else . . . "

It was working. Eli was almost off the horns of his dilemma. To renounce the program did indeed seem foolish. It was sentiment that had almost taken hold. But a scientist needs to be beyond sentiment. His gifts, as Kondorf had said, were something he had a responsibility to. He was obliged to use them—

He looked up startled. Kondorf's hand was on his shoulder.

"I feel for those two people just as you do, Eli," Kondorf was saying. "My God, I'm not exactly heartless, even if I am just an administrator"—he smiled at his small joke—"but, look, who were they before? Tillie, a lonely spinster in a village library drying up into dust along with her books until the aneurism hit. Floyd Gibbs, a three-times convicted felon. Neither of them anything to anyone. Even themselves. In all sincerity, could they possibly have achieved a greater meaningfulness?"

"Achieved—"

"Even Tillie. Your failure has taught you what to avoid next time."

"Next time—" Eli was having trouble with his breath.

"A new—an exciting new candidate has arrived. A prostitute, but rather unique. What if she were your breakthrough, Eli?"

Eli only half heard. He was seeing beyond the words.

CHAPTER SIX

CONNIE HAD been right. It was *Last Year at Marienbad.*
Death in Venice. The kitsch of the Sorrento Inn took hold
of this couple who under any other circumstances would
have hooted down the possibility of their being be-
witched by the enchantment about them. Ordinarily
they would have regarded it as so much persiflage, okay
maybe for the decor of a West Side Manhattan bistro
hoking it with Tiffany fakes. Of course, what was simmering between them couldn't have hurt the illusion;
perhaps it even made for a synergistic effect.

For her, her past blurred. All that had happened was
forgotten. It was as if some elegant, lorgnetted matriarch
in rustling taffeta had pointed an imperious finger, ordering a new perception of herself. "You are what you
are. Here. Now. Tomorrow can't take this away."

Dinner was eaten almost silently. Everything hushed,
as if commonplace words might shatter the fragile spell.

The dining room was dark wood, potted palms, crisp

white linen and heavy silver service. The staff as well as the other guests seemed wraiths, removed from them by a soft scrim. Even the soft laughter and the tinkle of crystal seemed swathed in folds of memories so delicate they might at any moment have blown away.

Phil had made the stronger effort to resist what was happening. What did this Art Nouveau charade have to do with a tumor excision? Was this a deliberate stroke by Elias Nunn? He couldn't believe that. The man was no charlatan, anything but. Was it an artfully conceived psychological analgesia for the patient's benefit? If so, he conceded it was bizarre but ingenious.

Here again, his guesses were wide of the mark. Phil's presence hadn't been anticipated, and it had created something of a panic in Washington. Some strongly wished that the surgery on the new candidate be scratched at once since her escort's presence violated the hard and fast rule, constituting a threat. Word then arrived that Elias Nunn was making problems. The question arose whether he would stay with the program he had begun. Everything seemed to be coming apart. No new candidate was available, and even if there was, the usual investigation would have taken too much time. Reluctantly, the word was passed along. Go. Operate before the scientist did another of his one-hundred-and-eighty-degree turns. His constancy to the program was a sometime thing. As insurance, a lesser of evils, the handling of the intrusive New York surgeon was passed into other, less discreet hands, who conceived of the stay at the inn as part of an overall plan.

The sunset, of course, was beyond control of Washington. It was a spectacular, and they saw it sitting on the wide veranda in cane rockers. A huge burnished sun went down into a sea of pale turquoise; and it was that moment when the birds—all nature—stilled for the great event of night's coming. He took her hand. They rose and walked slowly across the terrace away from the inn.

The sloping terrace was a riot of purple bougainvillea and orange hibiscus. They followed a path of white gravel that sloped down, leading them beneath a wooden arch called in Japan a *torii*, a gateway to a Shinto temple. Night-blooming jasmine, meanwhile, cast its net of perfume about them.

It was almost dark as they came to a wooden glen of aspens and willows, the path encircling a dark pond in which the first evening star was reflected. Giant koi, feeding on insects, rippled the dark water, hoping, no doubt, that the two visitors had come prepared for a handout.

They stopped.

Facing each other in the gloom, their bodies came together, their mouths hungry. Searching. And finally feasting. . . .

Later in her room, atop the four-poster, her legs high and about Phil's neck, she was certain . . . however improbable . . . that she had found something that deserved to be called love. She tried to suppress her difficult breathing so as not to disturb the new-found quiet in her. She was almost sure the incessant gnawing of the demon in her had at last stopped. It was too good to be true, a dream long ago given up, yet here it was now, finally achieved. She knew—she was certain—she had, for the moment at least, the very best, and she also knew it was more, much more than the mere physical thing which had just happened between them. The orgasm upon orgasm, which for once she hadn't had to fake.

"One thing I promise," she told him.

"Yes?"

"I'll never forget your name, aphasia be damned." She whispered it. "Phil . . . Phil . . . Phil."

He held her close, and it was all she wanted.

Eli had gone from the director's office directly to the lab section of the Center, where research was conducted. There was no neatness or order to the place. Complex apparatus of every sort, every modality of the physiologist's art, was represented. Highly skilled anatomists, biochemists, behavioral people, molecular scientists—all were synchronized as a team conducting carefully controlled experiments upon almost every form of life— except human. This ultimately was left to the neurosurgeon. It was here in this sanctuary, when he was most troubled, that he found some relief.

Eli was of the school that tended to hold that the functioning of the brain has its source in electro-chemical energy, and that even intelligence is directly proportionate to the mass or number of brain cell connections. He was in a corner of the large, littered laboratory now, peering into an electron microscope at a sea slug's primitive nervous system, neuron-stained by the Golgi method. The DNA within the large nucleus was of particular interest to him, since he knew it synthesized the protein on which the life of the cell depended. As usual, his concentration was complete, all else wiped from his mind as he made a series of notes written in that illegible scrawl, the despair of his staff.

He felt relaxed, relieved. That other business had become too much. He had overloaded. He shouldn't deal with such things, he knew. Practical decisions were not his strength. He never bought the right socks or shirts, he was a pushover for any eager salesperson. Moral decisions were the worst, tending as he did to view everything in black and white. Usually here, too, he "fell on his ass," as he put it. However abstract, and even applied, science was comfortable territory. Everything extraneous was proscribed, yet there was room for creativity. How often he had sworn to stay away from everything else, even politics, which often put him into messy situations in spite of the personal rewards of public acclaim.

As he fine-tuned the focus of the delicate apparatus, the view of the cell's nucleus sharpened. It was at this moment that the resolution of the problem he had recently left came into sharp focus.

His head lifted away from the eyepiece, his eyes already holding a kind of gleam. Almost the look of revelation.

He knew what he was supposed to do. It stood out vividly clear in the pure light of laboratory-nurtured virtue. His appetite for rightness felt at once appeased. My God, he thought, how blind. How could he seriously have thought of any other course? Initially, there might have been some excuse, but the first failure should have turned him off. His thoughts went to Tessa. If she knew what the program really did to people, she would say, of course, how else could he live with himself?

Closing down the microscope's mechanism, he replaced the specimen file into a cabinet. Returning to his office, he hung up his white tunic. The technicians in the outer lab looked up from their benches as Eli hurried through. Something's up with the old man, one of them thought . . .

The hang-glider barely moved in the darkening twilight sky. Eli, driving the coast road, pulled over and stopped the car to watch. The sight was painfully beautiful as something inside him seemed to soar with the craft.

He recalled what he knew of the ancient Greeks to whom aesthetics and virtue were so vital. Korndorf, he remembered, had spoken about gods and godliness. The soaring of the spirit, he now felt, was the alchemy that transmuted men into something like gods. But virtue didn't come cheaply. The hang-glider was now touching the beach at water's edge. . . .

He found her in the large kitchen with its greenery and glistening copper over the stove. She was dismembering a chicken. Rosarita, that Toltec monument of stone, was doing the vegetables. The *arroz con pollo* for that evening was to be Tessa's first try at it, even to the measuring out of the beautiful saffron.

He swept her into his arms. Rosarita, across the room, began grinding chili in her precious mortar with intense concentration. Tessa, aware of the woman's embarrassment, felt uneasy. Rosarita had been with Laura Nunn for a long time, and was considered part of the family. When Tessa had come into the house the housekeeper, of course, had concealed her feelings, but Tessa had picked up on the woman's disapproval.

But Tessa wasn't one to put up with bad feelings, not in her own environment. And in time Rosarita, with the instincts of a woman raised in a mountain village, perceived the qualities of honesty and forthrightness in Eli's new wife and came to respect her.

Tessa drew him out to the oak-beamed, white-plastered hallway. There, happily going along with his exuberance, she was shortly caught up in his passion. Never one for coyness or fake shyness, she was the one who led the way to their bedroom . . .

"Okay, Eli," she said softly, "tell me."

They were their first coherent words after. Those other wild sounds she had made a few moments before were part of a more basic language.

"Tell you what?"

"Something good's obviously happened. If I'm to expect this each time—"

"Something happened—"

"Something good."

"Good," he said.

The window was open, the sunset was beyond. The

same sunset that Connie and Phil were quietly contemplating not too far away.

Good, she repeated sleepily, half smiling . . . It had been different this time. There had been less of that driving urgency about his lovemaking which she sensed was his insistence, his way of saying that their age difference was of no consequence. She knew he fought against the convention: who was young, who old. In his passion he would be pleading to disregard the looser flesh, the hair whiter, and the diminishing appetite and recovery powers. This evening was the way she had always wanted it. The way it should be. Nothing to be proved. A fulfilling experience in itself.

"Tell me," she said.

"Later, maybe," he teased. Getting up from the bed, he urged her to dress quickly.

Kondorf didn't consider his next move reprehensible. Good executive that he was, he was simply preparing a fallback position. How, after all, could he trust Eli Nunn, who spun like a weathervane?

Therefore, no sooner had Eli left his office than he reached for the intercom switch. "Get me Doctor Jelke," he said. . . .

Richard Jelke had won the enviable position as Eli's chief assistant after fierce competition among the nation's brightest neurosurgery residents. The job was said to be the medical equivalent of being law clerk to the Chief Justice of the Supreme Court.

Jelke had been with Elias Nunn for almost a year, and by now a week didn't pass that he didn't reject some lucrative offer elsewhere. Not that he wasn't ambitious, professionally as well as financially, but he was held by the excitement and personality of Nunn as well as by the promise of the program. "My Gotterdämmerung" he called it, referring to the fatal fascination of the procedure for others as well on Eli's tightly knit team.

Eli had never ceased to impress them with the fact that a mere twenty percent of the brain's potential is used; their work, their dream, was to tap into that vast idle reservoir of unlimited powers. Their dedication to that dream was all-important, since he believed they were on the point of a breakthrough.

Richard Jelke was hooked. Committed and bound to that moment. No sinecure, no promised wealth or security of good life could entice him away. He came to believe that if the breakthrough did happen after his investment, he could never forgive himself. And so he remained the brilliant protégé of Elias Nunn. . . .

Kondorf leaned over to pour another margarita from a silver pitcher into the glass on the low table between them. They were sitting beside the pool at the director's luxurious home. They had played several sets of tennis, jacuzzied, followed by a swim. Wrapped in heavy toweled robes, they lounged side by side watching that by now familiar sunset.

"You play a nice game," Kondorf commented casually, concentrating on refilling his own glass. It had been a difficult game for him—not to win but to lose. He had played the hustler's game.

"I only wish I had more time for it," Jelke laughed.

"Who doesn't?"

Even more casually, a few moments later, Kondorf asked, "How do you find the program going?"

Ah! Here we come, Jelke thought. Norville Kondorf's reputation at the Institute for intrigue and manipulation hadn't escaped Jelke, who neither condemned nor condoned it. Since his own therapy, he tried at least to be careful with value judgments of others. So he accepted the director as he apparently wanted to appear—sincere, gracious, and forthright. He hadn't been fooled by the sets of tennis he had been allowed to win, nor even by the invitation itself. He was well aware that within the Institute's hierarchy, the director might invite him to a large Sunday party for drinks, but nothing like this. So obviously there was a motive. He sensed he was about to know what it was.

To the world, even to his staff, Elias Nunn was pretty much the fearless scientific genius. The staff accepted his eccentricities as the prerogative of his eminence. Richard Jelke felt, with a certain justification, closest to him. Closer perhaps even than the man's own wife. And not even he suspected or sensed the character flaw in his idol whom he loved as a father and whose perfectionist demands he put up with.

Thinking it best to be cautious, Jelke casually replied, "One step back, two forward—one hopes. You know the problems, I'm sure."

Kondorf nodded, and Jelke now ventured to say, "Is it true we're about to have another candidate?"

"A woman of thirty. She's arrived."

Jelke knew the program was on the line. A success was required. It was essential, in fact. And it would have to be even more dramatic than Floyd Gibbs.

Kondorf read his thoughts. "You've no doubts, no hesitation toward the program?"

"My God, no. Would I be here otherwise?" Jelke thought it wouldn't be a bad idea to remind the man of the offers he regularly received.

"And, of course, the privilege of working with and learning from the maestro," Kondorf said lightly.

"True."

The director said he was curious about what it was like to work with Elias Nunn. "What percent skill would you say it is, what percent instinct? I'm really curious about the man. I know him, of course, but not the way you do."

"Instinct. Flair. Call it what you want, he has it."

"In abundance," Kondorf agreed.

"As Boswell once put it, 'The quality which feels more than it knows.' "

Boswell, Kondorf thought. The young squirt's giving him the classics. However, he said, "Exactly, the question is, how unique is it? How does one know one has it? You, for example. How do you feel about yourself in terms of what separates the great from the ordinary surgeon?"

What was the man getting at? Jelke wondered. He no longer felt as secure as he did. The director's eyes were on him. A reply was expected, he knew, but he didn't know quite what to say.

"Please don't be modest," Kondorf went on. "Too much is at stake for any false posturing."

"I consider myself good. First-class. Not Elias Nunn, but first-class."

Kondorf nodded. "I consider that a fair evaluation, Richard."

Richard! Jelke thought. I'm Richard now.

"And to get better," Kondorf continued, "even to know if you have the flair, the instinct, you must find out. Tell me, Richard, is it true what I've heard? I mean that our genius in residence keeps certain of his moves at the table a secret?"

The director had touched a sensitive point here. Jelke had suffered a good deal during those moments when he suspected that Dr. Nunn not only didn't share certain things with him but seemed deliberately to hide certain subtle fine points in their work. He was aware of what megalomania attributed to many great surgeons. The fastest knife in the west one day might not be the fastest. Some hotshot kid coming up fast and so on. He wondered during those gloomy moments whether Elias Nunn thought of him this way.

"As far as the procedure is concerned," he said evenly, "only one hand can guide the probe."

"To be sure," Kondorf said, "but have you ever been allowed to be that one man?"

"In the lab . . . with animals—"

"No, no, I mean to do the procedure in an operating room."

Jelke was suddenly visualizing the procedure . . . the infinite delicacy involved, the many precise moves required . . . a miscalculation, an infinitesimal error of judgment or going in where an "insult" meant instant death—or what had happened to Tillie Harper and Floyd Gibbs. He felt suddenly chilled, and knew it wasn't the evening air.

He heard Kondorf say the words, "The question is, could you? Could you handle it?" But the full impact of them hadn't yet reached him. It was too mind-boggling. He had speculated with the idea, of course. But it was no more than a fantasy. A daydream.

"With Doctor Nunn's permission, if he stood by—"

"No, no." Kondorf smiled, and recalled the incident known around the Center as the Yamaha Affair. Shortly after Eli's marriage he had bought for himself and Tessa a pair of Yamaha XS-11's and would roar up to the Center each morning in helmet and tinted glasses. "It may not be known," Kondorf went on, "but I put a stop to it. I spoke with his wife one morning and explained her responsibilities. The point is, Richard, what if he does some other damned foolishness? He's not that young. A coronary in the sack is a possibility. Anywhere. What I'm saying is the program must be protected and on the basis of my confidence in you, I consider you the heir. The natural heir of Elias Nunn."

Silence. Far off, against the setting sun, Jelke could see

a fishing trawler returning from the sea with a flock of terns and gulls following in its wake, swooping and diving to feed on the catch. Their shrill, piercing cries reached up to the poolside terrace. Jelke suddenly felt even more chilled. In fact, freezing.

CHAPTER SEVEN

ELI'S SELF- AND PUBLIC-IMAGE were often compatible. He didn't lack for public testimonials, frankly finding each a needed confirmation of his worth, enabling him to deal with his guilts.

He wasn't a religious man in the dogmatic sense, and yet he sincerely believed that Man was made in the image of his Creator; that to harm, destroy a single human being was wrong. Pretty phrases such as "equality" . . . "brotherhood" . . . "all men are created free and equal" he felt abstract and therefore meaningless, since they demanded no personal responsibility.

He drove the freeway now with Tessa beside him, thinking he had allowed Kondorf to bludgeon his conscience. It was to serve his own purposes, to be sure, but they were blatant lies. Those cliché phrases—"order from chaos" . . . "pursuit of scientific knowledge"—bromides to stir up the enthusiasms of first-year students, but no longer, damn it, would they cloud his future actions. A terrible mistake had been made . . . except wasn't the history of science a history of mistakes? One admitted it and got on to something else. There was little doubt that cortical stimulation other than as a research instrument was wrong, in spite of its allure and promise. So he must walk away from it. If the genie was out of the bottle, okay, it was part of the research process . . . but let others go on with it, not him. He almost smiled. At this moment he felt very, very noble. Very *right*.

"Aren't you going to tell me?" Tessa asked.

He reached into his pocket and with a flamboyant gesture drew from it a small envelope that he held out to her. Switching on the map light she examined its contents.

"Oh, Eli—"

"Yes, my dear?"

"This—"

"Is no more than proof that study, hard work and clean living have their reward."

"You've been called a miracle worker."

"Is there any possible doubt of it now?"

A well-known rock group was playing that evening in a nearby stadium. The evening had been sold out for weeks. Several nights previously she had mentioned it to him in passing, not suspecting it had even made an impression. He handed it on to his secretary, who in turn mentioned it to the proper person, and two tickets arrived by messenger.

They sat unrecognized amidst the tumult offstage and on. Tens of thousands of young bodies seemed suspended in a sea of electronically amplified sound. To him it was bedlam, but Tessa loved it, feeling more at home than at one of his functions.

To his unsophisticated ear what he was hearing had nothing to do with music. Still, he let his senses be caught up in the effects of multicolored strobes and lasers lashing the stage and the arena itself. He submitted to the spectacle, felt carried along with it.

Involved as he was, he was hardly aware that at one point the music, at least the sound of it, had stopped. On stage the group persisted in their attack on their instruments. Just the sound had been cut off. Somewhere a pop bottle crashed. Whistles, hoots and catcalls. Anger, with the potential of igniting into something serious. At this point the speakers screeched with an overload and a voice boomed over them:

"Would Dr. Elias Nunn please come at once to the security office?"

For a moment Eli couldn't associate the message with himself. "Eli!" Tessa said, clutching his arm.

"Doctor Nunn," the speaker voice said. "Please stand."

His first thought was of some promotional gimmick he had unwittingly subscribed to by requesting the tickets. He sat stiffly.

"Doctor Nunn." the voice went on. "It is urgent . . ."

More whistles, boos, and Eli, realizing it could be getting out of hand, slowly stood up. One of the roving spotlights caught him in its beam and held him there. Others joined. Two or three T-shirted jocks, part of the security setup, converged on him. Others ran up and in a few moments formed a wedge, put Tessa and himself within it and rushed them to the rear.

Red lights flashing, sirens screaming, a squadron of CHP officers on motorbikes provided the escort. The old Volvo with another officer at the wheel showed her class.

Eli, seated with Tessa in the rear, at one point felt a rush of pride in her. He leaned forward to see the odometer needle quivering at a steady ninety.

Tessa sat staring at the road ahead, clutching Eli's arm. He could feel the tension in her. The cavalcade took the

freeway south, all other traffic peeling aside for them.
"Eli . . . ?"

"I don't know," he said truthfully. "I've no idea."

He had no intention of diverting the driver's attention; the latter, however, after a hairy maneuver, muttered a grudging compliment to European cars. "They stick to the road like dog shit," was what Eli thought he said.

They wound their way through the Institute's grounds at barely diminished speed. Ahead was the Center's compound with its sentry station. The guard on duty waved the procession through. It was late. Eli noted the unusual activity. Lights illuminated the Center's main building, nurses and technicians were hurrying in and out.

A security guard flung open the car door before the vehicle even stopped. "This way, sir."

Eli hurried inside, Tessa having to run to catch up. The second-floor corridor was bustling with unusual activity. Head nurse Mary Chatterton, seeing Eli, rushed toward him. He noted wisps of her hair straggled out from beneath her starched cap—if anything signaled the unusual, this was it, he thought.

"It's Tillie, sir," she said, the normally unflappable voice shrill, her eyes wide.

A door had been opened down the corridor and Eli and Tessa heard it for the first time. A piano. Piano-playing . . .

But it was playing that Tessa, who had a degree in music studies, found incredible. Never had she heard anything like this before. It was beyond anything in her entire musical experience. They moved—no, they were drawn—toward it.

In the control room technicians were at the console and monitors. Each knew his job, there was no unnecessary talk. No one even looked up as Eli entered the cramped room. After a quick glance about he peered down through the window to the room below.

Tillie Harper sat at an old upright piano which had somehow materialized in what had been a starkly bare room. Her fingers seemed to blend with the keys, evoking music of such incredible beauty and originality that those within earshot, whatever their sophistication in the art, found . . . "stunning" was the only word to describe it. It was neither classic nor jazz, yet its tone and rhythms encompassed both. One moment the sounds cascaded in whispering, caressing notes and chords, the next they crashed and beat on the eardrums, evoking primal resonances.

Tessa, her complexion bleached of color by the fluorescents, stood at the rear of the control booth, out of the way of the workers. Her eyes were closed and her lips drawn to a tight line. From time to time she opened her eyes to see below a frail, gaunt woman in a bizarre wig all askew, seemingly possessed. Pathetic thin fingers raked the keyboard. Black, white keys—singly and in combinations—were struck, hammered upon, caressed gently as they explored not only the possibilities of the instrument but of human experience far beyond it.

Eli, pushing his way back toward his wife, had to shake her to arouse her from her rapture. Aware of her knowledge of the art, he asked, "What's she playing?"

She could only shake her head.

"Answer me," he insisted. "It's important . . ."

Tessa slowly turned her head to him, wiping tears away with the back of her hand. "No one," she said, "has ever written such music. It's—believe me—impossible. Just impossible." With this, she moved away from him to listen undisturbed.

Tessa felt herself in a transcendental experience—she could hardly breathe as one moment the woman lifted her to sublime heights, the next catapulted her down into the agonies of a Hieronymous Bosch hell. The man beside her was of no consequence.

He stared at Tessa, then grabbed at a passing technician. "What happened?"

He was told that about an hour and a half before, this same technician was at the console, bored, and at the prescribed intervals feeding Tillie the proper short-wave electric charge. Certain slight changes had been noted in the EEG responses, but nothing was attributed to it. These reactions had happened before.

Then slight, sustained quiverings in her body appeared. The technician had summoned Mary Chatterton. As they watched, the movements became more pronounced. More general. Her hands made spasmodic movements. She had turned from her place at the wall to begin flailing her arms. The nurse had thought it a convulsion of some sort, but another technician, summoned from the next room, had the perception to suggest that her movements in some way resembled a pianist's, although one gone berserk. Despite the protests of Nurse Chatterton, he had the initiative to insist that a piano be found and brought in.

"Where was it found?"

"In the residents' lounge at the clinic building."

Eli nodded, making a mental note to commend the technician for his actions. Someone touched his shoulder. Turning, he saw Norville Kondorf, smiling a smile to split his face.

"Eli," Tessa was saying, "it's what you had meant earlier, isn't it?"

Exhausted, both still in shock, they were now slowly driving home along the coast road.

"I mean about the good," she went on. "You said something good had happened." She shook her head in wonder. "What understatement."

"You were impressed, I take it."

"*Impressed?* My God!"

But if she knew, if she really knew, he could not help thinking . . .

Five nameless-to-the-public men constituted the Committee on Bio-Energy in Washington. Their namelessness was appropriate since it would serve no purpose to give them names. Their expertise was in different areas, yet all performed a common function in an obscure committee.

One or two lived in fashionable Georgetown, the others in Chevy Chase. Violence had no role in their lives, their only brush with it fleeting, imaginary, as when after dark they hurried from lobbies to waiting limousines with apprehensive glances about them.

Phil Carlino heard the phone in his suite from Connie's bed. He glanced at his watch. Eight in the morning. Quickly he calculated it was still five to him. Nevertheless, he gently disengaged Connie's arm, climbed from the bed and, slipping on his shorts, went to his room.

"Yes?"

Natalie Burnham's cheerful voice greeted him. "Doctor Nunn would like to see you before he leaves for surgery."

"I'll be there," he said.

"The car is waiting for you."

Five men, two career public servants, the others brought in from banking and industry, had been selected to constitute the committee by reason of their expertise and executive abilities. The appointment at first proved unexciting. By Washington standards, it appeared a dead-end, with neither status nor glamor. Cortical stimulation seemed another egghead enterprise. Dutifully, they applied themselves to the logistics of creating the Jenifer Frumkin Institute, and even brought in several multinationals to form a consortium in order to share the great expense. This was to keep the nosy General Services accountants from questioning too deeply. The corporations were enticed into the project by the potential of good public relations, being in bed with the government in a research and development project so altrustic on the face of it. Besides, as a write-off, it would cost nothing.

Cortical stimulation (CS, as it came to be called) then flared into a high-priority program, and what had been dull, prosaic staff work had assumed an entirely new importance.

Shaved, showered and dressed, Phil returned to Connie, still asleep. Looking down at her, he indulged some special fantasies . . . Mom, I'd like you to meet Connie, the woman I love. She's sort of a, well, by trade, I guess you'd say a whore. Catholic? No, mom, she isn't Catholic . . . Heavy, he thought, *very* heavy . . . but he'd face that when the time came. He'd have to. He had trouble visualizing Connie and his mother in her kitchen cooking up an *osso bucco*. Of one thing he was certain, though . . . he loved this special lady . . . He regarded her, sleeping. She, of all the women he knew. Why did it have to be her? The men she had known—nameless and probably faceless—who'd parade before their bed each night. A Panovision de Mille production accompanied by whisperings, groanings, sighs punctuated with climactic "oh, yeahs," "that's *it* . . . " An X-rated recital. Could he handle it? Could she?

The five were family men. They played tennis or golf on weekends, one or two jogged, and all worried about their weight and cholesterol intake. They knew Washington. They knew just how and when to use the telephone, especially now. They acquired stamps for their letters and memos: "Top Secret," "Eyes Only." As government employees, words such as "kill," "murder," "assassinate" were simply never used; they bespoke criminal activities, which in turn implied responsibility. Even the word "conspiracy" would have appalled them. And yet, here, now, a situation presented itself which they agreed threatened the all-important program into which so much hope and effort had been invested, and for which they would be held accountable. Under this intolerable threat they resorted to the ultimate rationale—"national security"—and immediately the ugly words they shunned became less ugly. Euphemisms were not even necessary, since discreet words were mentioned to discreet people—professionals—and the latter went off and made appropriate moves and contacts. All that was required of the five was to scour files and correspondence for any incriminating evidence or culpability.

Awaiting Phil beneath the inn's porte cochere was the same black limousine with the same uniformed chauffeur. As Phil came down the steps, the chauffeur swept around to open the car's rear door.

Phil said, "I'll sit beside you." Ever the ethnic democrat.

"That won't do, sir," the man called Arthur said.

Phil looked at him closely. There was the tight smile, but he sensed something else behind it.

The message had gone north, beyond Washington's marbled halls and carpeted offices. It rapidly found itself in a small, midtown restaurant in Manhattan noted for its *Spedino Romano* and where the proprietor greeted the patrons with a "Mister Bob" or "Mister Joe." Intimate, yet properly respectful. Words were whispered into the ear of an elderly, much-honored guest whose total involvement seemed given to his *spedino*.

The car climbed the hills; the road became bumpy and signs of habitation grew less and less until finally they all disappeared. They were traveling in raw country high above the Pacific.

Phil had become increasingly uneasy. He leaned forward toward the driver. "Where are we?"

"Shortcut."

He glanced up to the rear-view mirror. The man's eyes were on his. He knew he was in for trouble as his early street conditioning, long unused, asserted itself. He looked about at the bleak countryside. Adrenalin churning, senses sharpened and alert, he vividly recalled the moments before the Bleecker Street gang made one of their sporadic forays into his neighborhood.

The car slowed. Through the windshield he saw another car parked in a clearing just ahead; and he could see two men move away from it, away from the car and away from each other in a highly professional way. Unhurried.

He didn't wait. He grabbed the door handle and yanked at it. Nothing. He went for the other side. The same. He was locked inside. Looking to the rear-view mirror again, Arthur was now smiling. And at the very moment he started to reach for him with both hands, the glass partition separating them came up. It resisted his efforts even to kick it through.

Good soldiers that they were, Carmine de Marco and Rafaele Tocco found the job distasteful. They felt absolutely naked—this business of doing a contract with no weapons, not even a length of rope or an ice pick. Instead, some character had met them at the airport and handed them a small case inside of which was a loaded hypodermic.

"Sure, I know how to use a needle." Carmine de Marco had said. "But you want to blow him away or give him a rush?"

The man had calmly explained it was no ordinary drug. Rafaele Tocco explained he didn't like to leave persons about to talk. "Exactly the point," the man from the Center explained. "He won't remember his own name ever again. And what's more no one can ever say a finger was laid on him."

"Amnesia," Carmine de Marco said, to the stranger's surprise.

"Permanent," the man replied.

Carmine de Marco and Rafaele Tocco, if not entirely comfortable, seemed appeased.

The struggle was brief. Three professionals made short work of Phil's strangely weak and ineffective efforts to resist being dragged from the car.

Looking down at him lying in the dust, they felt a certain contempt. Phil's size and something about him suggested there'd be more resistance. "A pussycat," Arthur judged.

Phil lay on the ground, breathing hard. His eyes were watchful with apprehension. He saw one of the men step back. Now he was taking a syringe from its case. Phil saw it glisten in the sun, especially as the man held it up to give it a squirt. "You worried he'll get air in his veins?" his colleague remarked.

"Hold him," the man with the syringe ordered. Arthur the driver and Rafaele Tocco kneeled on either side of Phil.

"Doctors are junkies anyhow," Rafaele Tocco said. "I

got a cousin that's a doctor in Union City. Junkies—their own pushers."

Arthur was now sitting astride his chest, pinning his arms. Phil's eyes followed the course of the poised needle as it came down.

It happened all at once. Simultaneously his body arched, dislodging the chauffeur, and at the same moment his foot lashed out against the hypodermic, smashing it. Phil was on his feet now, and as the three startled men converged on him, he lowered his head and charged one, who fell back, tottered momentarily at the cliff's edge and went, screaming, over. The sea birds, startled from their nests, joined their screams with his until his were lost.

Now two men came at him. Arthur the chauffeur was one. The other had disobeyed orders. He now produced a switchblade, which flicked open. Phil noted he held it expertly, lightly, in the flat on his hand.

He had no choice. The almost sheer cliff at least offered him a slight chance, and he took it. He slid, rolled, tumbled, snatching at outcroppings of rock and brush. The speed of his fall diminished and finally, halfway down, he stopped altogether. He lay on a small shelf of shale and disintegrating granite, breathing heavily, not daring to look up. He shrunk his body as close to the cliff as possible.

The two men above could see nothing because of an outjutting of the clifftop. They could just barely make out the sprawled body of Rafaelo Tocco lying among the rocks, the incoming tide tentatively reaching to it. The movement of one leg was because of the wash, not because of life.

"Climb down," the man from the east said to the chauffeur. "See if you see him somewhere." He offered the knife. "Use it if you do."

Arthur looked down the cliff again, leaning over as far

as he could. "He must have gone clear down to the water," he said.

"We got to be sure."

"Then you go down."

Carmine de Marco glanced over the side, calculated the chances of a man taking that dive and surviving, and decided his contract was completed.

CHAPTER EIGHT

NEITHER TESSA nor Eli slept. Side by side, in the privacy of their own thoughts, they lay impatiently awaiting the first signs of dawn. Things to be done awaited them. Important things; and never had a night seemed so long.

During the long night Eli had once again flip-flopped. How did he feel about it? Did he regard himself with scorn for weakness? For his being unable to take and maintain a position? No. He rationalized it as an attribute of his special scientific mind that could explore an avenue of approach, one hoped the proper one, with total commitment; however, should it prove the wrong move, he believed there should be no hesitation, no wasted effort in pursuing it further out of vanity or stubborn denial of incontestable facts.

That night he had put the question to himself again and again. How could he have forgotten the brain was his whole life? Where else could he replace his commitment to those fifteen hundred grams of tissue? The challenges it presented were, face it, his reason for existence. As a lover knows each crease and fold of his beloved's body, he knew the curves and wrinkles of that sublime organ so neatly divided in half. Right hemisphere, left. A world, a universe unto itself. The human brain to him incorporated that metaphysical concept known as the mind, and what more satisfying exploration could there be? Everest? Space? What search could compare to it?

Even aware that total victory in that search was beyond achieving, certain facts had already been established. Here was an organ possessed by the most primitive African pygmy, yet it had more elegance, more sophistication and complexity than the most modern computer. *Homo zinjanthropus,* sitting on his haunches on some veldt devouring berries, had been equipped with that same exact organ with not the faintest perception of its capabilities; even as today modern man could not conceive of its potential for tomorrow. As Koestler had written, the brain is a luxury organ developed in advance of its possessor.

Eli believed that the future of the human race, as well as its past, was programmed within the human brain; that man's understanding of reality itself was still only by sensory recognition, which in turn could be described as nothing more than the exchange of certain transmitter substances within the organ. That night he had asked himself what greater miracle could there be? And by what impulsive madness could he ever have thought to divorce himself from it . . . ?

As Tessa scrambled eggs at the kitchen butcher block, he went through the morning's ritual of lining up his various vitamins.

"Eli, how is it I never heard of Tillie Harper?" I mean as a musician or concert pianist? She's certainly good enough to have been noticed."

"Once, years ago," he said, smiling as he did, "she was a member of a small Gilbert and Sullivan group in her town. They'd gather about a piano and sing 'Tit-Willow' and such. She was the pianist, and not a very good one. This is from her own description of herself from our workup on her."

She paused with the eggbeater. "And that's *all?*"

With a certain satisfaction, he said, "That's all."

"Eli . . ."

"Yes?"

"Could I come with you today?"—her voice sounded indifferent, as if it meant little—"To the Center, I mean."

"You know better than to ask."

"I'm asking."

"Outsiders aren't permitted—"

"Am *I* an outsider?"

"Anyone not on staff is," he said. He went on to mutter something about being sorry about it . . .

"I was there last night—"

"It was crazy then, discipline went to hell—"

"Eli, I'd like to hear her again." She tried hard to keep her voice from sounding strident.

He knew she was looking at him. He knew precisely the expression she was wearing, her small mouth drawn into a drawstring effect. He gave his total concentration to the last pill he was gulping, anything not to have to confront her.

"If you like," he said, "I'll do my best to smuggle a tape out for you. A tape of her playing." He could hear the testiness in his voice.

"I don't want to hear a *tape,* I want to hear *her.*"

He didn't care for this at all. God knew he was irritable, too, what with the excitement of the night before and not having slept. The last thing in the world he wanted was a scene. He knew her rare black moods, usually at the height of the mixed blessing of her periods; he knew too long how how she could dig her heels in. He decided to get out. To hell with the eggs and toast. His head was already at the Center. Kondorf had spoken of the arrival of that new candidate. He eagerly anticipated the biopsy on her, what it would say. If the prognosis was bad, a malignant glioma, for instance, what permanent value would the procedure have, even if successful? And yet, how often he had wished the prognosis was negative so that in this way he would mitigate his sense of guilt.

He was almost out of the kitchen.

"Eli."

He turned, his face set. "I'm sorry, Tessa, but even you aren't excluded from regulations—"

"You and your regulations . . . the refuge of tight-assed people with something to hide . . ." And suddenly she was aware of something very changed in the atmosphere between them . . . she couldn't name it, because how could she possibly suspect that what she was picking up were his own dark forebodings about his work . . . ?

He had never entirely recovered from what he had done to Tillie Harper and Floyd Gibbs. Could he ever again handle it? He was subconsciously anticipating the next CS procedure, what dangers, and worse, he would come up against.

As they glared at each other, her face suddenly softened. She came to him, reached up and kissed his cheek. "I'm sorry," she said.

"That's better." He smiled. In a moment he was gone. Thoughtfully, she looked after him.

"I'm expected by my husband, Doctor Nunn," she said, smiling winsomely at the guard in the sentry house.

She had dressed slowly, giving Eli time to be off, then driven the stationwagon to the Institute's parking area.

From there she had walked to the Center compound.

"One minute, ma'am," the guard called after her. "I'll just put a call through."

"I'm late," she called back, continuing on. She didn't get very far as the man was now beside her, touching her arm.

"If you'll come back please, ma'am," he said politely but with sufficient pointedness.

"I said—"

"Yes, I know, ma'am."

She played out the bluff as best she could, finally asking the guard's name, as if he might expect a reprimand. No use. A second guard had appeared and was standing a few steps away in a watchful attitude. Again the man before her said he would phone.

"Don't bother," she said, haughtily turning to retrace her steps.

Why was she doing this? she wondered, while studying the traffic pattern through the sentry gate from a safe distance. What was there about that incredible woman and her even more incredible music that was making her do this unpleasant thing in defiance of her husband? The entire situation seemed unreal. The night before had been magical . . .

No, it had happened, she decided, and I must see, hear her again . . . She thought of the song of the Lorelei, luring sailors to disaster. Was there disaster in this too? In fact, could anything so sublime not have its terrible price?

Technicians and nurses all wore ID badges, she noted. A group exited from the compound, laughing and chattering as they made their way to the nurses' quarters beside the clinic building. Tessa followed them to a locker room where they changed their uniforms for street clothes. Selecting a nurse whom she thought had the closest resemblance, she forced open her locker and hurriedly put on her uniform with the plastic ID affixed to it.

Keeping herself concealed in the vicinity of the sentry gate, she watched until a group of nurses going on duty passed through. The guard glanced at them only perfunctorily. She now ran forward, as if hurrying to catch up with her colleagues. The guard hardly glanced up as she passed.

Walking past the nurses' station on the second floor, she felt her heart pounding. The corridor was now still. Empty. The night before it had been the scene of frenetic activity.

No one noticed anything. Now she felt in the center of a brightly lit stage. Where was the music? The woman must be resting, she thought. No, it was those heavy doors which would muffle any sound behind them. They were closed now.

But which door to open? She had her choice. She couldn't recall which one she had previously entered. Conditions were so different . . .

She chose the first. Grateful that the heavy door swung back silently, she found herself in a small foyer. The few steps at the right, she recalled, led to the control room. The other door with its latched bolt so anyone inside couldn't emerge must be the room containing Tillie. Quietly she slipped open the bolt and slowly entered the room.

A black man with heavy features and wide, staring eyes sat in a plain wooden chair. His huge torso was bare to the waist. Glancing about, Tessa was puzzled by the haphazard condition of papers and charts covered with incomprehensible writing and symbols. The man sat rigid, unaware of her presence. Indifferent to it.

She found herself drawn to him. Staring down in fascination, she came to realize he was less a man than a shell of a man. And there was the profusion of papers all about. Certainly it must have something to do with him, she thought. Could this be an equivalent to Tillie Harper's music?

Turning to steal from the room, she glanced up toward the large one-way glass, praying that whoever was behind it was occupied with something.

Outside in the corridor once again, she lost no time scurrying through the adjacent door. In a few moments she realized she was again with Tillie Harper. There was the upright piano in the otherwise bare room, and there was Tillie herself, standing motionless in a corner, facing the wall. She seemed somehow tinier to Tessa—as if the music she had created had increased her stature. Now the head was bowed and appeared to be regarding her feet in fixed fascination.

With both hands Tessa gently managed to turn the woman about. It was as if she were manipulating a mannequin. But it was the face, the dead face, which appalled Tessa. There were the same staring, lifeless eyes she had seen in the black man next door. The same detached, remote look.

"Tillie," she said softly, urgently, "Tillie, I've come to hear you play. Do you hear me? *Tillie . . .*"

No response. Unaccountably, she felt angry. Cheated in some way. She was determined to carry the woman to the piano if necessary. But at that moment an alarm bell somewhere outside jangled. The door burst open and nurses, technicians and security people were already pouring into the room. She kept pleading with the woman she was clutching to wake up, to acknowledge her in some way. Security later reported that prying the women apart was an awkward, very difficult job.

At about this moment Connie Keenan was being escorted by Natalie Burnham through the busy lobby of the Institute's clinic. It was the lobby of a typically busy hospital, much coming and going and a busy information desk manned by a middle-aged volunteer lady in pink. Physicians and staff people were somehow easily distinguishable from visitors or those there for therapy either as in- or out-patients. There too were those sitting on vinyl chairs or couches who had the dazed, exhausted look of having been there for hours, perhaps all night, waiting for the outcome of some crisis on an upper floor.

An attendant was emptying overfilled ashtrays and a Mexican madonna used her shawl discreetly while nursing her child.

Beside the small gift and flower shop was a door with a large sign: ADMISSIONS. Ms. Burnham, carrying Connie's two small traveling cases, guided her through.

"Sign this, please—that." The intricate, unreadable forms were shot before her almost mechanically by a stout woman with the compassionate air of a funeral director.

Connie had been puzzled. She had awakened to find Phil gone; however, there had been the note and the single red rose. The note explained he had an appointment with Doctor Nunn and that he would see her shortly. He also had written "I love you." It made her feel warm. Secure. A delicious new feeling.

She put her signature to whatever was put before her, hardly listening to the woman or bothering to understand the legalese of the wherefors and whereases.

Waiting for the elevator car in the crowded lobby, her everpresent escort beside her, she experienced a vaguely familiar sensation. An adjustment was happening within her, a psychological cleavage, a splitting of her consciousness so that in effect she perceived herself as standing back, witnessing what was going on. Her senses were dulled, and there was no judging. It was as impersonal as watching the six o'clock news on the tube. It was even difficult to recall she had just signed papers consigning herself over to pain, shock, possibly death. Physically, she was feeling great. Never better, especially with the afterglow of the night before.

"Where's Doctor Carlino?" she heard herself say to Ms. Burnham.

"With Doctor Nunn, I'm sure," came the immediate smiling reply.

The crowd pressing in on her, also awaiting the elevator car, wrapped her in a kind of anonymity. She wondered about this odd detachment she was experiencing. Twice before, it had happened, she recalled. A common thread ran through them and she understood at once it was a merciful process of insulation, minimizing the imminent threat. The last time, it had been during the hospital experience back east. The time before, it had been years ago, the first and only time she had been busted as a hooker. It was among her first dozen tricks, and it was in a raunchy hotel room just off Lexington Avenue. The john had just got it off with her, and standing before her with his half hard-on, announced himself as a vice officer. She recalled how ridiculous he looked with his tool glistening in the bare-bulb light as he recited from a small card the Miranda spiel. At the time, it wasn't that ridiculous. The shock, the fear. Then came that feeling—the same detachment which stayed with her through the night court ordeal and what followed in the god-awfulness of the Women's House of Detention down in the Village . . . that living through the experience, yet not . . . some part of her untouched, unviolated.

"It was illegal, his ballin' you," the black girl in the blonde wig had said at the jail. "But consider it a compliment . . ."

"Eight," the elevator operator said.

The room seemed more modern, lighter than the dreary hospital she had previously known. The sophisticated equipment—the wall outlets for a host of gasses and the microphone pinned to the pillow—all reassured her. How does one die with all this?, she thought. Someone had kindly placed a beautiful floral arrangement on the table beside the bed.

She turned to Ms. Burnham. "Doctor Carlino was . . ."

Natalie Burnham patted her hand. "He'll be here."

Connie was thinking she was beginning not to like her ever-smiling and ever-pleasant escort, but couldn't quite say why. On the point of insisting that her cooperation would end unless she could see her own physician, an efficient pair of nurses entered. It seemed a signal for Natalie Burnham to leave. The set smile faded, and it was as if Connie Keenan had never existed as she left the room and the assignment.

"We'll help you undress, honey," one of the nurses said, coming toward her.

"I want to see my doctor. Doctor Carlino. He came with me." She stood defiantly. The senior of the two nurses glanced at her colleague. The latter turned and quickly stepped outside. Connie stood clutching a chair which she had swung between herself and the nurses. In a moment the younger nurse returned with a male orderly in white.

"Undress, please," the older nurse repeated. Her voice was sharp now.

"No."

Her struggle was futile. She was undressed, a coarse hospital gown tied about her, and put to bed. With the aid of a sedative administered by the senior nurse, she became increasingly passive. Her efforts to remain awake were of no use. Her last thoughts as the dark curtain fell were of Phil. She even called out his name. "Phil . . ."

Eli sat in his office reflecting on whether it was ever possible to "know" the brain of another. Before him were copies of Connie's blood workups, dye and CAT scan studies of her brain. Large X-ray plates were snapped in the illuminated viewer in front of him.

He sat back, a distant look coming to his eyes. It was characteristic of his method of working—to sit back occasionally and allow his mind to wander, beachcombing he called it—picking up the things of interest he came on. Answers, in some cases; new, deeper questions in others . . . Was it possible ever to know the brain of another beyond a certain point? What of the business of thinking, the emotions, sensations, all functions of that unfathomable organ? Could they ever be charted? Made predictable? Where did one start to do this? Wasn't there always Heisenberg's Principle to contend with? The very act of an evaluation changed the thing evaluated. Brain cells, like all living matter, were aggregations of electrons of given arrangement and velocity, and to attempt to measure them at any given moment changed their nature. Knowledge of the human brain could at best be no more than estimation, speculation, approximation—

His thoughts were interrupted by the call from the security office.

Tessa sat quietly beside a gray metal desk in the office of the security chief. She appeared disinterested in the activity about her as Norville Kondorf and the security chief across the room were engaged in serious conversation . . . the director speaking quickly, his forefinger almost rhythmically stabbing at the man in front of him. Occasionally they would glance toward the culprit, who was under the surveillance of a uniformed man.

Eli, rushing into the office, paused at the threshold to look about. His distress and the haste with which he had crossed the complex were clearly apparent. Everyone but Tessa turned to watch as he slowly crossed the room to his wife. "Tessa," he said quietly.

There was no response. He repeated it. "Tessa—"

Her head half-turned and her eyes drifted up to his. For a second he thought he existed only within the curiosity of those light eyes. The next second he somehow felt she was lost to him forever. He had become a stranger of no particular interest.

"Eli—" Norville Kondorf had come up beside him. "Eli," he again began.

Eli raised a hand, stopping him, then to Tessa, "I know why you did it, darling, it's all right . . ."

Her answer was to get up and leave the office. Eli was about to follow but Kondorf was saying something about he should be sure she kept her mouth shut. "It's your responsibility," he said, calling after him. "It's in your hands, Eli . . ."

He found her in the bedroom of their house throwing things into an olive-drab duffle. The clock-radio beside the bed was on full volume, blasting a Joni Mitchell ballad.

Eli had heard the music as he got out of his car. It had a special significance to him . . . During their first weeks of marriage she would somehow automatically turn the volume up to full whenever she'd listen to music of any sort, whether downstairs on their excellent sound system, or even in the car. It was the typical musician's need to search for every nuance in whatever was being listened to. Once or twice he expressed his annoyance, and she was immediately apologetic. There were several incidents in which she thoughtlessly did it again; then, almost at once, she'd laugh in her delightful fashion and say, "There, oh, Eli, I did it again," and she'd quickly bring down the volume . . .

But now it was on full, and as he climbed the stairs, the message was clear. He switched it off but now she hardly glanced at him as she continued emptying closets and drawers, stuffing her duffle.

"Tessa, please *listen* to me." He was standing almost directly behind her now.

She straightened and turned, and what he saw in her face was worse than contempt, even hatred. It was total indifference. The chill he felt was as if he were standing in the shadow of an iceberg.

"Let me tell you, let me explain—"

"What can you tell me? What can you explain?" Her voice sounded dull. "What can our savior say when it's out? When everyone knows he's a fake?"

"Please—"

"Please *what?*" Her eyes took on a detached, odd look. "The men in my life, how similar . . . cut from the same cloth. I hardly know if they were men, or something I dreamed up." She regarded him almost quizzically. "You know where you were alike? You all had one quality, and I outfitted you with the rest. Dressed you up, as if you were so many dolls, in qualities you lacked but I imagined. Qualities, virtues. I needed them, so I could love you, you understand? Do you *understand!*"

He shook his head slowly.

"You don't understand . . . 'Savior,' I called you. It's how I saw you. Can I forget that first time I saw you? How you looked? The things you said? 'If ever a savior was,' I said, 'there was how he'd look, those were the things he'd say.' Mister Noble, standing so straight and tall among all us mortal people. Jesus . . ."

The room became still. Somewhere on a lower floor Rosarita was using a vacuum cleaner. The sound was the single thread connecting him to his life, he thought.

"I am begging you to understand—"

"Understand? Understand *what?* I've been living a

Punch and Judy show? And who's my Punch? Who has he turned out to be? A fine fellow, to be sure. The best. Smack those others down. Everyone. So long as he comes off a prince of a fellow, what does it matter? So long as everyone's quick to pile on the crap . . . to shake your hand, buy you a drink, *honor* you—"

"No . . . no—"

"No? You don't see yourself?" she said with an intensity he didn't believe possible. "No, how could you? But it's time you did, you—you *murderer . . .* "

CHAPTER NINE

"YES, OPERATOR. Detective Angelo Carlino," Phil repeated, giving the number of a police precinct house in the Pelham section of the Bronx. "And collect, please," he added, knowing that this in itself would convey a sense of urgency to his brother.

Waiting for the call to go through, he considered his predicament with some detachment and even irony. If Angie, whose business was violence, could only see his little brother, bruised, scraped, his custom suit something the Salvation Army would reject. Still worse was the terror of the incident still churning in him as he stood in an outdoor phone booth in the parking lot of the raunchy hamburger joint a few hundred yards from the small, rocky beach frequented mostly by young surfers, the salt-corroded Coors sign above the rickety screen door a hazard to anyone passing beneath it.

As he waited, his eyes anxiously scoured the vicinity for signs of his attackers, who he was certain hadn't given up on him. If anything, he knew that as professionals, what had been a simple contract to be done with a minimum of fuss and personal feelings had become something entirely different.

"Officer Carlino is being located," the operator said . . . Angie, big brother Angie, who had helped him survive growing up on the streets. The others had the gang, he had Angie. Tough, mean-looking Angie, who used to nurse his roof pigeons with the tenderness of a mother. Angie the Mumbler had been his street name, and for a while no one contested the sky clear to East Broadway for his ever-growing flock, which he'd send up to gather in strays . . .

"Officer Carlino's been located on another floor," the operator said. "It'll be a moment."

"Thank you," Phil said, nervously jingling some coins in his hand . . . Mama fingering her rosary beads segued into a recollection of the chromo print of Jesus which hung just above the chipped, white-enameled bed that for years he had shared with Angie. The rain-stained ceiling had been his vision of a sepia-heaven where the Old Man himself sat seeing all, judging all while His Son hung there in benediction with his left atrium and ventricle so indecently exposed. Could this be why he had wanted to be a doctor almost as long as he could remember? A surgeon to suture that open wound? To heal the poor raw thing? . . .

A gruff voice, New York-accented, said, "Phillie?"

The anxiety was there, as Phil knew it would be. Family, he thought. How good it had always been. The comfort of it, despite the pain-in-the-ass moments . . . it was something he'd instinctively turn to, an old-world tradition he couldn't shed along with the rest . . .

"What the hell you into in California?" followed Angie's first words. The anger, Phil knew, masked the concern.

He ran through the situation from the beginning. He did it as Angie himself would do it. No adjectives, adverbs. Facts.

Even so, he could only think as he spoke, My God, it sounds like some sort of classic paranoia . . .

"Who is she?" Angie asked.

"A patient, I said, for God's sake . . ."

"Yeah."

Phil anticipated his brother's cynicism . . . it went with his job. He wasn't an easy believer. A woman who was not of his family, especially if she was attractive, was a slut until proved otherwise . . . "I'm not in drugs," Phil assured him, "and I'm not hung out to dry, Angie. I haven't even robbed a bank."

"Okay, okay."

"I just feel I'm in the middle of a . . . a conspiracy." He said the word as simply, as blandly, as he could.

"A conspiracy . . ."

It came back to him dully. He could visualize Angie's sallow face pitted from a bad childhood case of acne and not helped by innumerable batterings. When he didn't believe something, he'd suck at a front tooth, often noisily. He'd be doing it now, Phil thought . . . "There are such things," was all Phil could think to say.

"Something's in your favor, Phillie," was the unexpected reply.

"Like what?"

"Like the fact your apartment's been gone over." Angie went on to say that the maid had called his mother, who called him. "I went over and had a look. A professional job, although someone wanted to make it look different. Some of your hi-fi equipment is gone. What were they looking for?"

"I don't know."

"Your office was also knocked off. You keep drugs there?"

"Some. The usual. Angie, go back, please. To the office, I mean. See if there's the file on a Constance Keenan." He spelled the name.

"She's the patient you're with?"

"I was. I should be."

Angie asked for more information about her. Phil told him Connie was an interior decorator. He had no doubt his brother didn't believe him . . . Angie was asking who he knew in Washington who could be helpful. "Give me some heavyweight lawyer with muscle. Someone who owes you."

Phil mentioned the name of Senator Driscoll. He didn't think it necessary to add that he had clipped an aneurism for Amy Driscoll, the senator's wife. "He's a friend," he said simply.

Angie grunted. Cynic he might be, but he knew enough about his brother to know that if Phil said a person was a friend, the party would be a friend. Period. He asked for more names. People who knew Connie. Phil mentioned Doctor Ephraim and the superintendent of the hospital where he had met her. He said they'd corroborate his story.

"Listen to me, Phillie. Listen good . . ." Phil wasn't to travel or use any public conveyance. By no means was he to go anywhere near the hospital or the hotel. "Just find some beach girl. Hole up in her place and don't even go out for so much as a beer. Not until I say so. Clear?"

Phil said nothing for a moment.

"What is it?" his brother asked.

"I don't have the time," Phil said, going on to explain that his patient was scheduled for surgery at the Institute. "It's all got to do with that somehow . . . I'm sure. Someone just doesn't want me there. The question is—why?"

"You leave that to me," Angie said. "How do you like abalone?"

"What?"

"You're an amateur dealing with pros. You do what you shouldn't do and you'll move in with the abalone, and what good will that do your . . . patient? How you for cash?"

"Enough, I guess, for a few days at least."

Angie gave Phil a phone number to commit to memory. "You call me tomorrow exactly this time. I'll wait for you and I'll have more to tell."

Phil felt better as he left the booth. At least he was no longer entirely alone in the midst of his nightmare. Squinting against the sun, he scanned the cliffs in both directions. In the distance he could see a light Cessna towing gliders at regular intervals over the sea. The umbilical released, the gliders soared in graceful spirals in a fair imitation of the hovering sea birds. All in all it was quiet. Peaceful. Another sunny beach day in June. Far in the distance he could make out a cluster of white buildings on a high point, and he suspected it was the Institute. Even now she could be there, he thought; and only his brother's warning prevented him from going there to see her, to find out . . . to *do* something . . .

Eli might have described his own condition as ex-sanguinated . . . life seemed certainly bled from him. It was no more than an hour since Tessa had left, and he sat in his study trying to gather together the pieces of his suddenly shattered life.

Here was his sanctuary. The heavily-draped room contained shelves of well-used reference books and periodicals reflecting his wide-ranging interests. A single wall was given to memorabilia. Here were hung diplomas, testimonials and autographed photos of himself in the company of some of the world's most prestigious personalities. His career's history in souvenirs.

How have I gone off?, he asked himself. Been less as

a man or as a scientist than I should be? The measure of success—prestige and reputation—the good things I've done and stood for even outside my work, aren't these some indication of what I am . . . ? There were failures in the program, to be sure, but failures are to be expected in any research. Who can say I ever lifted a scalpel for personal gain? Murderer, she said. My god . . .

He thought of the countless opportunities by which he might have enhanced his wealth, his reputation, just by the use of his name. He'd turned them away. In his misery, and self-pity, he had to find *some* good rebuttal to her charge . . . murderer, indeed . . .

Norville Kondorf found him sitting in the red Moroccan chair which rested over the Bokhara that took the chill of the wet seasons from the Spanish tiles. It appeared to the Institute's director that the man was contemplating his trophies . . . reliving achievements and moments of glory?

"Your patient's being prepped, Eli," Kondorf said, looking down at the tall figure shrunk into his chair. Eli looked up slowly. "Science is waiting," he continued, aware of the hyperbole, gesturing toward the trophies. "All that was just a prelude to this moment which can be the capstone to your career . . ." Even as he spoke he felt a growing anger . . . his patience running short. Damn him, how much more do I have to indulge him, massage his ego? He went on, "You know, Eli, brilliance of your sort is very parochial. How is it one of you geniuses hasn't come up with a formula: talent—genius, if you will—is inversely proportionate to your qualifications as an asshole?"

Eli smiled, in spite of himself. "You're showing promise as a wit, Norville."

"I refer to your knowledge of women."

"I know, I should be beyond the sexual *Sturm* and *Drang*—"

"Your age has absolutely nothing to do with it. What the lady sees in you is your larger-than-life image. Your fame. Your reputation. The charisma surrounding Elias Nunn. If you think it's anything else, my friend, you're deceiving yourself. And if she says otherwise, she's deceiving herself as well."

"It's too bad we can't ask her," Eli said.

"She'll be back sooner than you think. I'll leave you with this: Stay in your funk and you'll surely have blown it with her. You do a successful CS and she'll love you more than ever. Oh, *yes* . . . despite all that's gone down, your cause won't be hurt one bit. Believe me . . ."

Kondorf had touched on something which had often bothered Eli. What if he had been a broker—a merchant? How would Tessa, others, have thought of him? How would it be? Would he have attracted the respect, attention, even admiration he'd become accustomed to? Even if he had achieved success, money, would it be the same when he entered a room? To feel that certain hesitation, the eyes turned in his direction? Delicious moments as if he were, say, a movie star. The interest, the excitement he felt he aroused in women. The women. Those soft, pliant looks that made him forget his years and quickened his juices. And Tessa. As the man suggested—would she have happened, come into his life, if he were Elias Nunn, auto-parts dealer? And even if she somehow did, how would it have been when he found he couldn't deliver that encore? When his balls ached and his so-called member said enough already. Would she have said, "It's okay, dearest. Don't fret, you've made me very happy. Good night."

Even to himself his words seemed ridiculous, though

his style almost carried it off. "I'm not altogether unattractive," he said half-smiling.

Kondorf's smile was mocking as he replied. "Eli, you're beautiful—"

Raised, angry voices came from somewhere in the house. A crash and something breaking followed.

Both men hurried out of the room to find Tessa struggling with two men in the front hall, who found she was almost more than they could handle.

Eli ran at them, ordered them to stop. Tessa was determined to break loose. She was a wild thing, swinging her hands, kicking out. But eventually the men restrained her.

"Let her go, damn it," Eli repeated.

But it was Kondorf's word that brought her release.

She stood now on the staircase, the men a step or two below. Wild-eyed, she glared at them, but it was clear she couldn't pass. The men, in strangely inappropriate sports shirts with Hawaiian motifs which hung loose over their trousers, took a stance at the foot of the steps which she wisely didn't challenge.

"Please go upstairs," Kondorf said. "To your room." His tone was low, but with something new in it. Even Eli, surprised, stared at him. "If I say the word, they'll take you there."

Tessa turned to stare at Eli. He was contemplating Kondorf, who suddenly seemed another person. The tone. The authority behind it. Tessa abruptly turned and ran up the stairs. Kondorf made a small motion with his head and the two security men turned and left the house.

"What the hell was *that?*"

"You can't handle her," Kondorf said, "and we're not about to let her go off saying things she shouldn't. The program can't risk that—"

"She's going to be a prisoner here? Our own house . . . ?"

126

"That's your word. After the next procedure is done, we'll see. As I said, it may all change." He glanced at his watch. "Come on, Eli."

Eli slowly shook his head. His mouth was a grim line. Kondorf said, "Have it your way," turned, and left.

In his car, before starting the engine, Kondorf reached for a radio-phone. "This is Doctor Kondorf," he said to the Institute's operator. "Get me Doctor Richard Jelke."

Richard Jelke's small stature was a point of sensitivity to him. He had learned to compensate for it in several ways, among them two-inch-heel lifts, also selecting his wardrobe so as to avoid horizontal lines or stripes which would have a tendency to flatten him out still further. The matter of his silky fine blondish hair foretold still another problem to come. He was thinning out there, and one could predict by the time he was forty, Richard Jelke would be interested in a "piece" or a transplant job. His greatest compensation for these imagined inadequacies, among others, was the fact he was a brain surgeon, a profession which elevated anyone to a near-godlike status. Some felt he must have had this in mind when he chose neurosurgery as his profession; nevertheless, his insecurities persisted.

He could easily have been a little Napoleon, if he ran true to type. There certainly was the opportunity, particularly since his wife Gwenn was a born sufferer, a slight, febrile victim of life in which everything spelled disaster. She came from old Detroit money, original investors in Ford; and if she wanted Dick to leave the Institute and go on to bigger, better things, it was as much to appease her people who thought she had married down, not only socially, but it turned out to their dismay Richard Jelke was half-Jewish. And yet Dick was kind, tolerant with his Cassandra. Despite her fragility, both physical and emotional—his "Dresden doll," he'd call her in moments of affection—he secretly envied her style. Often, directly after their infrequent lovemaking, he would think, honey, you even fuck elegantly.

The phone call from Kondorf affected not only his own life, but those about him. To be sure, directly after his visit to the director's house, he had the sense he was on call, that the day was imminent when he'd be asked to take over the CS procedure. And with this sense his life changed . . . he became edgy, apprehensive. As a neurosurgeon he sincerely felt he knew as much about the anatomy of the human brain as anybody. Nevertheless, it was as if he were once again a med student cramming for a tough exam. He hit the books. He haunted the clinic's medical library. He made a point of lunching with the neuroanatomists at every opportunity. They wanted to discuss tennis or the cornering capabilities of the Mercedes versus the BMW, in the best California tradition, anything but the human nervous system, but Jelke persisted, asking, "Do you believe in the Jones, Nauta, Goldman theory that connections from one region of the cortex to the other terminate in patches with a predictable periodicity of about a millimeter?" or "Do you go along with Mountcastle's observation that that feature supplies profound insight into cortical organization . . . ?"

His companions would go cold, look down at their food and decide the guy was a bore to be avoided.

He procured the workup on Connie which had been shipped from the hospital in the East, and he studied it with an intensity he had never before given to a workup. He was especially interested in the CAT scans where the tumor could be plainly seen. It appeared to be a benign meningioma with its small island of calcium, and the characteristic hyperostosis, accumulation of bone. Of course, only biopsy could give verification that it was benign. The craneotomy and subsequent resection weren't major concerns. Things normal, it would be a run-of-the-mill procedure he had done innumerable times before, either as chief surgeon or as assistant. His fear, his dread, was what was to follow—the cortical stimulation . . . the going further into the recesses of the brain with its infinite possibilities for catastrophe.

His wife Gwenn now had good reason to suffer. He became unbearable, unfit to live with. Not only she suffered, their eight-year-old son Jeff did, and he suffered most of all. . . .

And then had come the phone call from Kondorf's car, and strangely enough a calm came over him.

Answering the page, he took the call at a nurses' station at the clinic.

"Yes, Doctor Kondorf, I'm acquainted with the patient's workup . . . yes, I'll have another look at it . . . yes, I'll do the CS . . ." He asked if anything was wrong with Doctor Nunn, and the answer was vague, noncommittal. He didn't persist.

Hanging up the telephone, he looked about him . . . nothing had apparently changed . . . all was as it should be . . . the traffic, the nurses doing their incessant writing which seemed to occupy them more than their patients' needs. No one paid him the slightest attention. He, though, had changed. He canceled his rounds.

"Is anything wrong, sir? Are you all right?"

Jelke stood at the threshold to the study, having been admitted by the housekeeper. He had been a guest at the Nunn's several times and knew the general layout. Eli's appearance suggested he was anything but all right.

"Come in, Richard," Eli said, getting up with some difficulty from the chair. "Somehow I think I was expecting you. Coffee?"

"Thank you." He followed Eli's glance to the thermos

on the tray. Eli made no effort toward it, so Jelke poured. "For you?" he asked, looking up.

"No."

"I asked if you were all right, sir."

"Oh, I'm all right." Eli studied his young assistant, saw the tension and suspected the cause. "You've been asked to perform the CS?"

"Yes, sir . . . it's why I'm here, to tell you . . ."

"You're the logical choice. In fact, who else could?"

Jelke's face was grim. Miserable. "The fact is, I don't want to do it."

"Did you say that to Doctor Kondorf?"

Jelke shook his head slowly. "It isn't fair—"

"*Fair?* What's fairness to do about it?" Eli's voice quickly calmed. "It follows in a natural order of things."

Jelke had come prepared to play out a role, a difficult one, especially since he felt trapped and on poor footing. He had to play it by ear, he knew, in reaction to Eli Nunn's reaction. "I've thought of the possible consequences . . . what if *I* succeed where Elias Nunn failed, what if the probe, by luck—happenstance—nicks the right part of the right neuron in just the right way? Nothing at all to do with my skill or ability—"

"And what we're looking for happens," Eli added. "The patient becomes a very special person with facilities intact."

"Exactly."

"I would say very good. Also, that you were very lucky."

"Lucky?"

"No?"

"There'd be no happiness—no joy—in it for me," he said. He pointed out that he considered every aspect of the program Eli's inspiration, sweat. "It's yours. Yours alone." His voice was rising. "Everyone knows it. I of all people know it. I would be miserable—"

"Oh, come on Dick . . ."

"Miserable. And what's more—ridiculous." Jelke had the words "Pyrrhic victory" on the tip of his tongue but thought that would be overdoing it. Instead, he lowered his eyes and said slowly, "Who knows better than I do the hours you've put into it? I've seen you. I know how dog-tired I was so I knew how you were feeling. You think I can just walk in, take over and get . . . lucky?"

Eli studied the young man he had brought along through the years. He liked him. In a sense cared for him. He was the vessel of much that he knew. He couldn't fault his ability or talent as a surgeon, and he was even aware of the many tempting offers he had turned down. There was no doubt in Eli's mind. Jelke was the best assistant he'd ever had. Once or twice, watching him take over at some less crucial stage of the operation, he had considered his work superb. In the O.R. he had everything; it was just outside where there were certain rough edges that might hold him back. The top neurologists and internists would hesitate with their referrals. There was the matter of his half-Jewishness that he'd heard of. Not that it mattered to him, God knew. But he himself had encountered that high wall of subtle prejudice, coming out of Boston U and later Bellevue Hospital in New York as he did. The doors opened reluctantly, and it took courage, good work and, unfortunately, above all—flair.

For several moments the room was silent, and Eli walked across to pour himself a coffee. Jelke watched intently, with fascination. For years he had studied the man, tried to imitate the grace, the economy of movement, that damned style. He was wondering how effective he had just been. He had thrown out the bait. Was the old man going to take it?

"Dick, tell me . . ." Eli began.

"Yes, sir?"

"What's the patient's name."

Jelke was startled by the question. Eli repeated it, this time adding, "Keene, or something?"

"Keenan."

"Ah, yes."

"Constance Keenan, also known as Connie Keenan."

Eli put down his coffee mug and approached his assistant. A quizzical smile softened his expression. "Isn't it odd," he said, "we hardly mention her, no less think of her? The patient whose care and condition should be paramount. Don't you think it odd?"

"Well, it goes without saying—"

"Without saying what?"

"Her care, condition and welfare is what it's all about —medicine, I mean."

"And the program," Eli asked quietly, his voice abruptly incisive, "how does the program insure her condition and welfare?"

For a moment Jelke was confused. What did this stuff have to do with the problem at hand? Only his fear of and respect for Eli prevented him from showing impatience. Almost as if he were in a classroom, he spoke by rote. He pointed out that all they did—every moment of their work—served the cause of good medicine. He mentioned the terminally ill patients he himself had kept alive by ordering support systems and chemicals and drugs and painkillers. "And yet all the while I knew it would have been a blessing to let nature take its course." He paused a moment. "I don't consider myself inhuman. Some sort of monster. My conscience is clear, I believe I was practicing good medicine. If it wasn't helping the particular patient, it was possibly helping other patients." He had made his point, he thought, and now he abruptly changed the subject. "May I ask a question, sir?"

"By all means."

"Would you care to tell me why you elected to drop out from this operation?"

A fair question, Eli thought. It deserved a straightforward reply. What could he say? So much . . . so much even beyond Tessa, who was mostly a sounding board for his own conscience. And all of it so contradictory. How did he justify dropping a project into which so much had been invested? He would have to find the proper answer, but now he only shook his head.

"Then, sir, may I beg of you—reconsider. If for only the very reason you just spoke of—"

"What's that?"

"The patient," Jelke said. "How can I possibly serve her the way you can? No one can."

Eli's eyes fixed on Jelke's. He saw in them a sincere appeal. Everything Jelke had said resonated in him. It *was* his program, damn it. No one else should attempt it, take the responsibility of failing . . . or getting, as it were, lucky . . . "We must think of that, the patient, I mean," Eli said. "Yes."

And Jelke knew he would do it . . . and knowing that, felt at once profoundly relieved, and profoundly disappointed.

CHAPTER TEN

OPERATING ROOM THREE at the Clinic was used mostly for neurosurgery, since its equipment included a microscopic viewer with a sidepiece enabling the surgeon and his assistant simultaneously to have a forty-power enlargement of the field in which they were working. Their view was transmitted onto an electronic wall screen so that others, especially the scrub nurse, could follow the progress of the procedure. A pair of large wall clocks gave both the actual time and the elapsed time of the operation, commencing with the first incision. The anesthesiologist tinkered with his various tanks, valves and support systems. O.R. Three was being readied for what was officially scheduled as a craneotomy and tumor resection; and while the surgeons in an adjoining section were changing into surgical attire and scrubbing down, the room was filled with casual banter and hospital gossip as everyone went about their respective tasks.

At this moment Connie was riding the gurney

through the long corridors. The Phenergan and Demerol were having their effect; her anxiety was gone, she felt fine. She was covered with a light blanket and strapped to the vehicle. Her shaved head was covered with an elastic dust cap designed with multicolored pansies. As the ceiling fluorescents streaked by overhead, she thought of the flashing neons of Broadway at night, a penny arcade, the Fun House at Coney Island. There was a hubbub of noises . . . voices, the paging system . . . Doctor This, Doctor That . . . all washing over her in a bland, incoherent jumble.

In the elevator the orderly pushing the gurney tried a number on a pretty young nurse. Connie felt amused by how she was ignored . . . Hey, buster, you're my chauffeur, please keep that in mind . . . Still it was as if she had no existence, had lost her identity . . . I could be a bundle of laundry, she thought without anger. Dirty laundry at that. She thought the thought quite clever. She felt satisfied with herself. Oh, I'm so clever . . . She would have laughed. Was she laughing?

"I heard of this new rib joint," the orderly was saying.

"I'm on a diet," the nurse said, "so buzz off."

Like the entrance of a movie star—the chairman of the board at a board of directors meeting—the smalltalk stopped with Connie's entrance into the O.R. The transfer from gurney to operating table was done expertly, with even a bit of help from her.

So nice. Everyone's so nice, she thought. Polite too. She had a flash of "21," the Four Seasons, the impeccable courtesy. A menu, mademoiselle? The veal paillard is excellent today . . .

Her head was clamped into a pin-headrest, the three stainless steel pins immobilizing. The dust cap was gone and her head glared, naked. A tentlike arrangement came up, shielding her from the lights overhead. Nurses adjusted sphygmomanometer cuffs and plastered a series of ECG leads to various parts of her as the anesthetist fussed with taping IV's into both her wrist veins. All this while Eli Nunn and Richard Jelke studied the large X-ray plates on the illuminated wall screen. Eli's voice was low, his talk technical, having to do with certain arterial systems between their plotted course and the tumor. Jelke understood his role in these "discussions," essentially audience for these soliloquies.

"Ready, doctor," Dr. Korsacker, the anesthesiologist, called over, and Eli moved toward the table, followed by Jelke.

Elias Nunn had, in a real sense, metamorphosed the moment he had entered the O.R. Worries had been left behind, along with doubts, fears and even his incessant moral conflict. There was as little room for those here as a stray staphylococcus. He was born again, as it were, the man in charge of this micro-universe, the captain of this ship. His authority was unquestioned, his judgments final. His was the ultimate responsibility in this world where life and death were the issue, and both in his hands.

For the first time in days he felt a burden lifted, and a peace went through him. He was in his element. All else—nothing. Thank God . . .

"Hello, Connie." He was now standing beside her. The scrub nurse behind him was adjusting his optic headset and light.

Her drugged eyes drifted toward him. His eyes were all she could see of him and they seemed friendly enough.

"I'm Doctor Nunn."

" 'Lias Nunn," she murmured drowsily.

"My friends call me Eli."

" 'Li."

He told her she would feel absolutely no pain. If she felt uncomfortable in the slightest, she was to say so. He explained further that she'd go to sleep for a while, then when she awoke, he'd need her help.

"Help—"

"I'll ask you questions. Ask you to do certain things, okay?"

" 'Kay."

Eli's eyes drifted toward the anesthesiologist. It was sufficient. They had worked together before and Lionel Korsacker knew precisely how Eli liked things . . . at what speed to bring the patient down or up. He stood at the patient's head in his tangle of stainless steel, of tanks and tubes, manipulating the cylinder valves, blending the compressed gasses or solutions alone or in combinations for this desired effect or that. A compliment from Elias Nunn was the ultimate, and Eli had once called Lionel Korsacker an artist, for which he was profoundly grateful.

"Count backward from one hundred, Connie," he said. "One hundred," he began, as he opened the valve of the IV allowing the anesthetic Brevitol to flow into her bloodstream.

"Ninety-nine . . . ninety-eight . . ." She managed to just about reach ninety-five, at which point he intubated her in case her tongue fell back.

"She's yours," Lionel Korsacker said to Eli, settling back with his respirator and gauges. Eli accepted the scalpel from the scrub nurse. The elapsed time clock began to move.

For a while it was the familiar ballet seen countless of times on TV screens. Hands moving with incredible dexterity, requests anticipated . . . a marvel of synchronization, an exquisite marriage of man and technology, and the center, the focus of it all, was a tiny area of human tissue. The only sound was the beep of the monitors, and the rhythmic respirator pumping.

Elias Nunn had his own rules of discipline in the

operating room, rules calling for absolute silence except for the business at hand.

He was cutting now through the scalp covering to reach the cranial cover. Jelke was ready with small pads, pledgets, with which he applied pressure to stop the bleeding so that the field was clear. The third pad did the job. The scrub nurse had the trepanning saw ready, and in a few moments the sound of the whine of bone being sawed filled the room. It took several more moments before Eli handed the instrument back to the nurse; with a forceps he then delicately lifted a section of bone the size of a half-dollar. A young resident surgeon waited with a watch glass into which it was carefully placed and given to the circulating nurse, who in turn handed it to a pair of technicians at another part of the room who went to work over it. The edges of the opening were waxed by the resident to prevent bleeding and oozing.

Eli glanced toward the anesthesiologist, was told "Stats fine." Eli did his bimanual examination as the anesthetist compressed the ventilating bag to breathe the patient. "One-oh-five over seventy. Pulse seventy-two," Korsacker said. "Bring her up?"

"No need yet," Eli said, glancing toward the blips on the oscilloscope machine.

Scrub nurse Williamson knew Eli would be needing a scalpel and a probe, and the instruments were ready as his hand reached out. Jelke held the coagulator, the resident the suction machine. The resident cleaned the field a bit, at the same time gently using moist pledgets so that the exposed tissue was continually irrigated.

There it was, Eli thought. The cerebrum, the outer chambers to the temple, with its fissures and convolutions. It was almost a religious experience to Eli each time he encountered it, entering the tabernacle.

Neurons were the building blocks of the brain, each with its single long-fibered axon and numerous short-fibered dendrites. Their very number staggered the imagination, numerous as stars in the galaxy, as some put it: the figure ten followed by approximately eleven zeroes, and each neuron connected to up to ten thousand synapses. A forest, a maze—with each single dendrite performing a discrete function whereby information is passed along chemically and electrically by mysterious transmitter substances. And all for one purpose: to enable the individual to survive, to know his environment and to react to it. And this aside from that mystical function called the Mind, with which we think, learn and remember.

He glanced up at the elapsed time clock. Twenty-two minutes had passed. All was in order. Another glance at the anesthetist fussing with his apparatus and gauges showed no problem there either. The heart monitor across the room beeped smoothly.

He went in.

In his mind was indelibly printed the precise course he must follow to reach the tumor by the safest, most expeditious route. The blunt instruments pushed aside the folds of tissue almost seductively . . . "Easy, easy, nothing to be alarmed at, I'll just be a moment here, this arteriole, we won't bother you, my dear, ah, careful now, so, just so . . ."

He followed the course of his movements through the optic system. Jelke, peering into the sidepiece, followed them. Others in the room glanced toward the oscilloscope screen and could see the sharply defined dark shadow of the instrument making infinitely slow progress into the recesses of the brain. The course had been computerized, so that when he made the slightest deviation, an alarm system buzzed harshly, a red light flashed.

It was one of his idiosyncracies that, like some musical

conductors, he would seem to be speaking to himself. It was a special rapport with the material at hand, in Eli's case—a human brain. Mouthing silent caressing endearments, warnings and placating supplications, his running dialogue suggested what he was confronting had its own personality that he could wheedle and deal with.

Jelke saw the bleeder almost simultaneously with Eli, who made room in the constricted space for the coagulator to touch the end of the oozing blood vessel, sealing it off.

The elapsed-time clock showed one hour and thirty-two minutes had passed. Connie was breathing unassisted. Lionel Korsacker was relaxed. The suction machine cleared the area, and once again Eli's head went down to the eyepiece after checking her vital signs with the anesthetist.

"There it is," Eli said quietly without looking up. Several minutes more had passed, but time in an operating room had that special distortion; minutes seemed hours.

"Yes," Jelke concurred.

Eli asked for a scalpel, and with eyes glued to the optic magnifier resected a tiny bit of tissue from the growth, the size of a small walnut. As Eli placed it on a watch glass, his assistant was busy applying the coagulator to stem the bleeding. The scrub nurse handed the covered watch glass with its specimen to the circulating nurse who in turn passed it to the runnurse who hurried from the room to Pathology.

Eli understood the anesthesiologist didn't care to keep his patients under heavy anesthesia longer than necessary. He also understood that once the brain had been entered, there was little if any sensation there, a seeming paradox, considering that it was the center of the entire nervous system. The Brevitol's advantage was that it was a quick, time-controlled anesthesia.

"Bring her up," Eli said.

Dr. Korsacker reacted quickly. As he shut off the flow of the IV, he extubated her, removing the device from her throat.

Eli and Jelke now stood away from the table, as they awaited the biopsy report. The resident had taken over the eyepiece of the scope, keeping alert for some unforeseen event.

"What did it look like to you?" Eli asked Jelke, more testing than seeking confirmation.

"As we suspected from the scan," was the reply. "Certainly neither an astrocytoma nor an ependyma."

"A dermoid," Eli suggested.

"I'd bet on it," Jelke said.

Eli nodded. Here was another dilemma. A benign tumor was obviously a blessing, a gift of life; and yet if the biopsy confirmed it, it was the signal to go to the CS procedure, since it had been determined that it would make little sense—indeed, be ghoulish—to create some form of genius in a subject doomed to live only a few months or less. Simultaneously there was the eagerness to perform the cortical stimulation, and the hesitation in the face of the risk of being responsible for a human disaster.

The intercom buzzer sounded. A crucial moment. All eyes on Eli, who had been standing close by, waiting for it.

"Doctor Nunn," he snapped into the instrument. For several moments he listened. Hanging up, he said to no one in particular, "Benign."

In leaving the area about the table, Eli and Jelke had presumably become contaminated. Gowns, masks and gloves were quickly replaced before they returned. Eli's eyes went to the anesthesiologist's.

"Up," the latter said, signifying that Connie was no longer in deep anesthesia.

"Signs?"

The nod suggested everything was normal, stable.

Eli came beside Connie and touched her arm. "We're at the tumor, Connie," he said. "It's benign and we'll be removing it, okay?"

" 'Kay," she murmured, her voice slurred from the medication.

The resection took fifty-two minutes, and wasn't as radical as had it been malignant. How much tissue to be removed was a matter of judgment. A metastasis wasn't a problem in a dermoid; yet it should be cleared out, as much as possible, lest the growth change in nature or even grow to impinge on some vital system. Delicate and precarious as it was, no undue complications presented themselves. Only twice did Jelke have to apply the coagulator to cut off excessive bleeding. The suction machine drained off the blood and other bits of sloughed-off tissue, and it was done.

Done, except not done. Ordinarily the rest would have been anticlimactic . . . the closing-up left to the assistant, he in turn aided by the chief resident. In this instance, however, what had passed was only prologue. The really hazardous part was yet to come, and all in the room were aware of it.

Cortical stimulation—CS, as the program was called—went even further beyond the paradigms set by Wilder Penfield during his surgical treatment for epilepsy. This adventuresome procedure was where the difficulties were encountered. Research was further stimulated by a Walle J.H. Nauta, who devised a cell-staining method proving that when a neuron is mechanically or electrically attacked, parts of it, fibers, are somehow dispatched to distant regions of the brain, where they take hold and develop. The trauma may destroy the specific neurons, but its new roots may inspire unforeseen, remarkable results.

Eli turned to the scrub nurse to speak a single word. "Electroprobe."

The instrument with its thin wire running back was instantly put into his hand. All eyes were on him as he brought the long, blunt-ended instrument toward the aperture in Connie's skull.

He knew precisely where the probe was and where it was intended to go. This had been planned and charted very carefully with Jelke's help. In the lab they had a computerized playback of where the probe had ventured into the cortices of Tillie Harper and Floyd Gibbs. Those loci would be scrupulously avoided.

"Connie," he said at one point, "can you hear me?" Other than the mechanical sounds, the room was absolutely still.

"Um . . ."

"Doctor Jelke will touch your right hand," he said. "There, do you feel it?"

"Um . . ."

In a few moments he had the probe in the motor region of the cortex. "Could you waggle a finger for me? Any finger will do."

Eyes were fixed on the hand, and when she tentatively raised an index finger, it was as if she had just performed a kind of miracle.

"That's splendid, Connie," Eli said. "Real splendid."

Eli moved the microelectrode half a millimeter. This time he pressed the switch on the device, sending a minute charge of current into her brain. Her left leg jerked in response. The course of the instrument was followed on the oscilloscope screen as it now entered into the parietal lobe. Again he depressed the switch. "What do you see, Connie?"

There was a moment's hesitation. "Light . . . light flashes," she said, her speech slurred. "A disco. Out of a disco like."

"Good, Connie," Eli said. "Very good." The micro-electrode penetrated further, not piercing but gently pushing aside folds, following fissures.

Eli subscribed to Lashley's commonly accepted theory that memory is not a function of any specific portion of the brain, this despite Milner's suggestion that certain memory processes lie within the temporal lobes such as the hippocampus area. He thought of memory as a distributed function. His own analogy was that of the hologram principle in which information is stored in a dispersed manner.

He was in the hippocampus now. "Anything, Connie?" he asked.

"The gardenias," she said.

"What about them?"

"They smell strong. Too strong," she said.

"Where are the gardenias?"

Falteringly, she described a modest house in a suburb of New York City, Flatbush. It was before her father had made his fortune. She described the house to the minutest detail. She seemed to be reliving her experiences in the house, her voice even taking on a childish timbre. Those in the room felt a sense of eeriness. She then began to resurrect actual dialogue . . . "I hate the smell of 'em, ma, they make me think of grandma's funeral . . ." Her voice rose, and the nurse at the sphygmomanometer announced a rising systolic. Connie apparently was undergoing the same emotions she felt at the time.

"How is school?" Eli asked, wanting to divert her.

Surprise came into her voice. "School?"

"Yes. Anything new going on?"

"Richie Meier says Mr. Horton has crabs because he scratches so." Her voice had become that of a twelve-year-old. "Crabs. Crabs. *Ugh.*" Now her voice turned singsong. "P. Kohn's Magic Café, P. Kohn's Magic Café . . ."

"What's that?"

"P. Kohn's Magic Café . . ."

"Yes, I know. What does it mean, Connie?"

"What does it mean? It means it's what life is. Living life. It's easy to remember it that way, Mr. Horton says. P for phosphorus, K for potassium . . ."

"Ah, yes."

"Life, life, there should be no strife . . ." she sang. Her tone changed abruptly. "Ferdie Parr's hands are big red crabs, he sneaked one on my toosh at fire drill . . . Ferdie, you stop . . . I'll tell Mr. Horton . . ."

He moved the electrode an infinitesimal distance away and at once she was silent. It was as if a stylus had been lifted from a record.

"Connie . . ." he said.

She stayed mute. Over masks glances crisscrossed about the room. He made a minute adjustment. A nurse dabbed the perspiration from his forehead. Once again he called her name, more sharply now.

Nothing.

Anxiety communicated itself about the room as he withdrew the microelectrode. Connie lay motionless, her eyes staring into the shield above her. He swung the microscope aside.

"Connie, do you hear me?" Eli said, coming around to her side.

Nothing.

The monitor's beep skipped once, then again.

"Eighty over fifty-three," Dr. Korsacker said, concern in his voice.

"What the hell," Eli involuntarily called out. What had gone wrong? There was no physiological reason for this. He was nowhere near the breathing control system, nor even the heart action. An infarct? The tiniest of embolisms? He didn't know, couldn't say. All he knew was, it had again happened. If she died, he doubted if even a p.m. would give the answer.

The monitor skipped a few times. Nurse Williamson reached for the already prepared adrenalin hypodermic. Dr. Korsacker had a mask over Connie's face and was twisting at the valve of a cylinder of oxygen. Eli was meanwhile lifting the lids of Connie's eyes, which had shut. He flashed a small light into them and what he saw there, the dilating pupils, startled him. The heart monitor tracings were flattening fast, the beeps coming in a slow arrhythmia, the alarm sounding reduntantly.

"Fifty over thirty," the scrub nurse intoned, holding her voice steady as she could as she took a blood pressure reading.

So-called heroic measures were begun. Asepsis was forgotten. All in the room had their tasks, and they were done efficiently and effectively. Electric shock stabilized the heartbeat, Dr. Korsacker's support systems took over. Connie's breathing, artificially maintained, became normal, and color returned to her skin, which had already taken on a bluish tint.

Jelke stood beside Eli with a watch glass in his hands. Eli looked down. In it lay the cylinder of bone taken from Connie's skull, but now affixed to it at its axis was a small stainless-steel protuberance of about two inches. On the underside of the bone, and attached to it, were a series of fine metal wires.

Jelke's eyes held a question.

Without a word Eli lifted the bone with a forceps, and with Jelke's help adjusted the wires in various portions of Connie's cortex. When it was done, the bone was carefully fitted back and the flap of skin was sewn back to cover it.

There were new sounds in the room as the support systems maintained their rhythms. Connie's eyes remained closed. She responded to none of the usual neurological tests.

"Show me a report on her EEG," Eli ordered.

In a moment it was brought to him. To all intents and purposes Connie Keenan was dead, and yet her brain showed life. Life which no machine could give her, yet life within very narrow limits. To all intents and purposes, it was no life at all since it was precariously suspended in a comatose state.

Still, it held a potential for . . . For . . . ?

CHAPTER ELEVEN

TESSA WAS hardly content to remain a prisoner in her own home. Since her confrontation with Eli, there had been complete avoidance of each other, which the large house facilitated. Moreover, he had spent most of his time in his study, even eating and sleeping there. The fact was, neither had a taste for another confrontation.

Her outrage at what she had seen at the Center grew in her, her imprisonment exacerbating her anger. And this built the feeling that she had only one course, to let the world know, which became something of an obsession.

From her bedroom window she could just make out the pair of guards stationed at one side of the property. From another window she could see the pair at the front. It was a twenty-hour surveillance, she observed, rigidly coordinated.

Plotting her moves carefully, one morning she managed to scurry aboard the rear of an old pickup belonging to the Chicano gardener. Burying herself under fertilizer bags, lengths of hose and other equipment, she lay there, her bitterness growing as she waited for him to complete his tasks about the grounds. What was she doing here?, she wondered. It was all so incredible. Amid the smell of wet burlap and steer manure, she went back to the events of that incredible day when it had all burst apart. She had said that the men who had been important in her life were somehow more contrived than real. But then so was her own life, her own happiness, she realized. There'd been music, wine, flowers at her wedding. But here she was hiding in terror beneath bags of cow manure. Wonderful.

The gardener and his son almost crushed her as they threw their power mower back onto the litter under which she was hiding. The pickup started and began to move off, but then in a few moments she heard a sharp command. The vehicle stopped. The older man was complaining in broken English that he had much to do and was late. The rear gate of the pickup clattered down, and in a few moments she was exposed. Her struggle was futile. The Chicanos watched wide-eyed with a certain fear for themselves. After all, they were Mexicans living close to the border. She was dragged down and returned to the grounds.

"Don't do it again, ma'am," she was warned with forced politeness.

She sat in front of the telephone in the bedroom, considering whom to tell her story to. Careful, she thought. Move carefully. Her first instinct was to call the police, in spite of the irony of it. For years police had been an unpopular part of her trendy vocabulary. Now she was leaning toward them for help. She drew her hands back from the instrument. "Jerk." She berated herself almost aloud. "They're together, they have to be . . ." She sat on the edge of the unmade bed, considering alternatives.

Calm it, girl, come down. You'll sure as hell blow it . . . Taking a few slow, deep breaths, she reached for the phone.

The managing editor of the local newspaper listened respectfully after she had introduced herself. She recounted what she had stumbled into. What she knew of it through her husband, who wasn't spared. She was careful—very careful to avoid speculations and judgments. Facts, just facts.

"Are you there?" she said at one point.

"I'm here, Mrs. Nunn. Go on."

As the words came from her, she began to hear them as if she were someone else. Wild, bizarre . . . It sounded like the bad plot of some late-night movie.

"Where can I reach you, Mrs. Nunn?" the editor said when she had finished.

With sinking heart she gave the number. Of course! If he troubled to make inquiries, where would that be? At the clinic of course. "Hey, fox, you in there with those chickens?"

"Listen," she said. "Understand this, *please*. I'm not paranoid. I'm of sound mind, although I confess I'm bloody mad. I've had no personal complaint against my husband until this. He's Elias Nunn . . ."

"Yes, ma'am."

"But now they have me prisoner in my own home," she began, indignation exploding in her.

"I'll call you back in a few minutes, Mrs. Nunn," he said, his tone flat, placating. "You'll hear from us."

"Thank you," she replied, thinking, You lying s.o.b. . . .

The next day, she had guests, short-lived. She had called friends in Venice, Los Angeles, who hearing the urgency in her voice, came at once. Mike Hausner was a bearded fellow in a Hang-Ten T-shirt with a gold earring in his left ear. He did socially satirical plaster studies somewhere between Siegel and Kienholz but in his own style, managing some success. The guards at the entrance had no specific orders to bar visitors—bureaucracy has its built-in oversights—and so Mike and his wife Katy were allowed to drive in in their white Jag convertible. Still, the guards weren't boffs and did go to check on the new development.

Mike was a tough character. Katy was serene, ever smiling, could find goodness in a garbage heap. The three poured from a gallon jug of Gallo Chablis at the swimming pool as Tessa began to tell her story. Her friends listened attentively. When she'd finished, the deadness of their expressions shocked her.

"We've been friends a long time, Tessa," Mike said, his voice somber.

"Oh, Mike—"

"A long time," he repeated.

"Yes, *yes.*" She felt a rising impatience with the reluctance she was sensing.

"I never met Elias Nunn," he went on. "Not until the wedding. Still I feel . . . I felt then like I knew him a long time." Tessa now was obliged to listen to a eulogy of her husband, a recital of the things Eli had said and done in their subculture. "He stood up there with us through heavy stuff . . ."

Tessa agreed but the bitterness—the irony—in her voice seemed lost. She was hearing echoes of herself. Eli's virtues as she had known and thought of them. Her own words even. It came to one thing. Eli was loved. Go fight city hall.

"It doesn't go down, what you're telling us," Mike was saying. "It don't go down at all."

"Why would I say this?" she protested. "How could I possibly make this up?"

Katy Hausner gently said, "When we heard you were

marrying him, we cried. Actually. Can you imagine Mike crying? We did. Both of us."

"Elias Nunn—come on, Tessa," Mike said, shaking his head.

"You saw those men at the gate as you came in," Tessa said grimly. "Cops. They're cops."

"So they're cops. Cops keep out tourists—"

"They're to keep me *in,* " Tessa shouted angrily. "Let's get in your car, see how far I'll get—"

"Honey," Kate said softly, "if he isn't doing you regular as you'd like—"

They were now both saying things, but Tessa wasn't hearing them. She felt a sudden loneliness. A chilling despair.

"Go away," she heard herself saying.

"You disappoint me, Tessa," Mike said.

"He's a flame," Katy said. "A flame, and he's yours. To say such things . . ." Her tone was a reproach.

As they were about to go the guards came quickly to escort them out, their faces red. They were about to say something when Mike said, "Take care of her, the lady seems to have gotten some bad, bad vibes . . ." He shook his head.

The guards looked at each other, seemed to be simultaneously relieved about something, smiled and nodded the couple to their car.

Hours later, in the kitchen having a glass of juice, Tessa heard Eli's car drive up, some doors slam shut, then nothing more. He had closed himself off again in his study.

That night she came awake, suddenly, unaccountably. Opening her eyes she thought the house was on fire. The ceiling glowed with the reflection of flickering flames from somewhere outside. Hurrying out to the small balcony, she looked down to the terrace adjacent to the pool.

Eli was throwing books, photos, framed diplomas into what was already a large bonfire. Great showers of sparks shot skyward with each batch. He'd watch for a moment then hurry inside to reappear in a few moments with another armful, which would feed the flames. Even from where she stood, she could recognize his most prized memorabilia, the contents of the basilica as well as books and papers.

Immolation, she thought. A self-immolation. She didn't, of course, know about his most recent failure that same day. Remorse, guilt, shame, she thought. In the distance she could make out the red glow of a McDonald's sign on the coast road. To Big Mac in the sky.

He's tearing apart, she thought. She tossed a robe over her nakedness and hurried below.

Standing some distance off, just beyond the perimeter of the glow of the flames, she watched in the semi-darkness as he stoked the flames with more and more souvenirs of past glories, honors.

"Hey, what's goin' on here?" A pair of security guards had come up running, their gaudy Hawaiian shirts now covered with dark thin windbreakers. They approached Eli, who regarded them bleakly, needing a moment to adjust. The flickering flames gave the scene an eerie quality.

"What the hell *is* this?" the other guard said.

"A weenie roast," Eli said, "what the *hell* do you think?" He went off to fetch still more material for his ritual.

Connie Keenan was a being in the clinical sense of the word, but her consciousness was of another order, one unrecognizable as normal consciousness. Something entirely new and original had happened to her. She was proof of what before was speculation . . . that life actually can exist on many levels. The number? It could be eight, seven—as little as three. Each a discrete lamination impinging on the next. What is considered our reality, responds to our five senses, is simply one of these layers, maybe the least important. Cognition is a major function of the brain, so that if one says "cow," or if one sees a picture of a cow, or the actual cow itself, or even hears its moo, we then somehow visualize a cow. Everything in the known universe has its accepted convention by which we face, recognize and deal not only with reality but with our emotions, thoughts and recollections. The wonder of Connie Keenan and what happened was proof of the existence of other realities as well, where physical laws didn't hold and all was as bizarre, and mind-boggling, as the interior of a black hole among the stars.

She lay in a bed that had been elevated to an almost sitting position facing the barred window overlooking often beautiful vistas she could see but not appreciate. Her own vistas were indescribably more beautiful. A large bandage, draped as a turban, encased her shaved scalp. This hid almost entirely from view the terminal which protruded from her scalp and which was the antenna receiving the short-wave stimulation sent to her brain at prescribed intervals, as it was with the other two subjects. The hope was sustained that she would do a Tillie Harper one day—unexpectedly come out of her coma. There were also various plastic IV tubes running from her arms to various machines outside the room.

She had her own fleeting thoughts and ruminations, struggling for some hold on them as they swept by, evanescent as wisps of clouds in the wake of a storm.

One such murky, fragmented recollection was that of a girl called Lucille with whom she had once shared a West Side flat during the early days of her hustling.

Lucille had come home one morning after dropping acid for the first time. She could hardly contain herself for the high she was feeling. Connie recalled asking her if she had picked up a ruby ring in an aisle at Bloomie's.

Lucille knew the jargon. She'd been through Hunter, Primal and est. Connie herself had touched those last two bases. Lucille's words came back to her now. Her fear had been complete, she had said. Experiencing it, there was nothing else to experience. Experiencing it to the fullest, she experienced a kind of death.

Heavy, Connie had thought at the time, and gave it no further thought. But now there were new insights and perceptions and the knowledge that the dread in death was the recollection of forgotten memories of previous death experiences. . . .

One morning it happened.

The technician at the console in the control booth admitted into her room a Latin cleaning porter with a heavy floor-waxing machine. The latter went to work and the white vinyl floor became even shinier as rhythmically the buffer was pushed back and forth. Paying no attention to Connie as she paid no attention to him, he hummed some ancient Jalisco melody as he did his work. It was just another sunny morning. Light reflections from the adjacent ocean danced on the ceiling. Feeling warm, he loosened the wool sweater knitted for him by his wife that he had left behind in Mexico. Touching it, it made him think of her with yearning.

The technician in the booth lounged back in his chair, thinking of the weekend golf game, more specifically of a troublesome slice he had developed and how he might compensate for it. The automatic timer pinged, and he reached across to his console to make the transmission. Doctor Jelke had ordered seventy millivolts in patterns of two milliseconds. The notch was somehow missed on the rheostat setting so that the voltage was seventy-three instead of seventy millivolts. The toggle was thrown and he didn't even look down into the room below.

If he had, he would have seen the woman in the bed

stir ever so slightly. Her eyes blinked once or twice and a liveliness came into them. Her lips parted a bit, then closed. Then once more, but now she began to speak. Her voice, however, was not her own. It was heavy, coarse—and what was more significant, it was in Spanish. It was an angry voice.

The Mexican cleaning man grew rigid. He stood staring at Connie. Disbelief, superstition, awe—these were evident in his posture. The handle of the heavy buffing machine fell from his hands, and then the machine scurried across the floor like a living thing. Cautiously he approached the bed, his normally dark face now pallid with shock. As he stared at her, she continued to rattle off in the foreign tongue, her tone bitter and harsh. The Mexican then slowly made the sign of the cross, backed away and ran.

The intercom system happened to be open; moreover, the tapes automatically spun, recording all that happened. The technician, alerted, at once summoned Dr. Jelke and whomever was available. As they assembled about her, Connie once again had become silent, reverting to her former unresponsive state.

Kondorf attended the hastily called staff meeting, grimly listening as the technical data unfolded. A nurse translating the tape explained that it was the voice of a peasant woman. "I think it might be a village in Jalisco," she said, adding that she happened to have relatives in such a place. She described it as part of a dialogue a woman was having with someone who would smuggle her into the United States. "From what she says, he wants seven hundred and fifty dollars American. She can only pay five hundred. That's for the baby too—"

"Where's that porter who was in the room?" Kondorf demanded.

Jelke explained that he had sent for him but he wasn't

to be found. "The security man at the gate said he had left, running. He hasn't come back. The chief custodian says he's probably an illegal."

"We'll never see him then," Kondorf said miserably. "What knowledge does the patient have of Spanish?"

Jelke slid a folder across the table to the director, who leafed through it impatiently.

"There's nothing at all in her background that suggests she knows the language," Jelke said. "Two years of high-school French, at which she wasn't very good, and three months of German, which she gave up on. Those were her language accomplishments."

"She might have picked it up later," Kondorf suggested.

The Spanish-speaking nurse nervously volunteered the information that whoever spoke on the tape must certainly have been a native.

No one at the meeting, including the Center's neurophysiologists and various behavioral scientists, could unravel the incident. There may have been those who had an inkling about a possible explanation, but for some reason they held back as they realized their theories would have been unscientific and their own credibility would suffer.

Jelke found Eli on the beach, sitting on a dune close to the cliff. It was a protected cove. The low tide had left the drying sand virgin and smooth, and at the far end the water washed over smooth rocks half submerged. Bits of kelp and mermaid-hair clung to the rocks, rising and falling gently with the tide.

Eli sat in this refuge, his back against the cliff, motionless as the rocks themselves, peering out to the horizon of the calm sea.

He had always felt a special affinity with the ocean. It was essentially the reason he had selected the house he called home, its closeness to the ocean. It put his head right, as Tessa might have said. The sky, the water— their ever-changing moods, never twice the same. Even in summer, during the endless sameness of the days, there were always differences to the perceptive eye. The sunsets were often breathless in their beauty as they brought out the full palette of nature's colors.

There was, too, the mystical bond between man and sea, some atavistic linkage to his beginnings. And this was especially true when he found himself in a black mood, a despairing introspection that helped bring up basic questions. Unanswerable questions, usually.

It was in this sanctuary that he had been putting questions to himself . . . including the ones having to do with his inconsistencies, weaknesses of character. He knew his need for being right, how even as a child he would run to the authority of a book or an encyclopedia to prove a point, and that special glow he felt when he could prove he had been right after all. He also suspected he knew where it began . . . with a childish need to win approval from his father . . . he considered how, in most instances, he had been able to disguise his faults. His name was mentioned with superlatives. His acknowledged genius further generated a reputation for infallibility, being right. And, damn it, he *had* fed this reputation with achievements. And yet, beneath it all, he knew something of the weakness of the foundation. In the quietness of such reflective moments there was always the undeniable truth.

At this particular moment, his truth-facing seemed to paralyze him. He had, in a real sense, destroyed three people. If at least the last had proven a success, the other two might have been forgiven by some strained logic, and he could be seduced to try and try once again.

Why? The question haunted him. *Why?* He had performed countless craniotomies. There had been the usual number of mortalities and even some few accidents of brain damage among them, but nothing like this, especially when the procedure seemed to be going well enough. His instruments were nowhere near areas which could create such havoc. He spent hours speculating on the possibility that some new yet unknown principle had become involved. He rejected out of hand the notion that it was something metaphysical, touching maybe on a mystical curse for having dared enter the temple for purposes frowned upon by some higher intelligence. He pushed such dismal speculations aside as preposterous. He wasn't ready for this. Not yet . . .

Rosarita the housekeeper had told Jelke where Eli could be found, but it was with some difficulty that he located him in the cove. After several moments of hesitation, he came to him.

"Doctor Nunn . . ." he said softly. He had to repeat the name before Eli slowly turned his head, squinting against the sun. His expression showed no recognition, so that Jelke felt obliged to say, "It's Dick Jelke."

There was no warmth, no invitation to sit down, stay, anything. Jelke felt awkward standing there, looking down at the man.

Finally he launched into the amazing news, describing in detail what had happened at the Center to Connie. Eli listened with no apparent interest. He made no comment.

Jelke wasn't even certain that what he said had been heard. "We know it's significant," he added, "but we don't know what to make of it." He told Eli that a meeting of the entire staff came up with nothing.

Legs feeling cramped, Eli got awkwardly to his feet. Peering at Jelke for several moments, he finally said, "She responded to the transmission?"

"In some way we can't understand."

"And without the transmission?" Eli asked.

Jelke's face became bleak.

"Nothing. Nothing, Richard, right? In other words, she's no better than the others."

Jelke shook his head slowly.

Eli turned to leave.

"Doctor Nunn . . ."

Eli turned slowly. He was several feet away by now. "Yes?"

"What do you think it means?"

"I've no idea," Eli said. "What's more I'm not sure I care."

"Shall I tell them you don't know?"

"Tell them what you please." Once again he was about to turn, but as an afterthought said, "I'll tell you what."

"Yes, sir?"

"You go back down there. You put a watch on all three, and the moment any one of them shows any signs of humanity unaided, without benefit of an electric jolt . . . a whisper for a sip of water, a single unaided step, a word, a look of *life* . . . bring this news to me and I'll be back with you." Then he turned and went off down the beach.

Jelke stood for a moment watching him, shook his head and started back.

Eli walked slowly now, looking down to the hard sand at the water's edge. He came to what appeared to be the remains of a child's mud castle being devoured by the incoming tide. He stood there watching as a wash of frothy water laid siege. A rampart collapsed, a dike surrendered and filled. Two more assaults by the incoming tide and little was left of the castle but a slight mound which he morbidly associated with a forgotten grave. A child's dream was buried here, he thought. Unmarked. Forgotten, probably even by the child himself.

And flooding back, like the sea, came his own memories . . . Saturday matinees at Poli's Orpheum in Bridge-port, hundreds of restless kids, noisy, scrambling for some position in the pecking order. No one paid attention to Kay Francis' dire predicament on the screen or how Warner Oland in his inscrutable mask would solve the unsolvable. He idly wondered what the association with his present attitude was and could find none. If the mills of the gods ground mysteriously, he thought, they were certainly no more mysterious than the mills of the mind. . . .

Continuing on, he walked slowly, the rising tide washing over his old tennis shoes. His head was stooped, and except for the fact that the hard sand held neither shells nor pebbles, he might easily have been mistaken for a shell- or pebble-hunter.

Suddenly he stopped.

Just ahead, two elderly men were scouring the sand for buried coins and other articles of value with the use of an electronic metal detector. Something in him seemed to vibrate at the sight. Slowly, almost cautiously, he went closer. The man with the device swept the sand in deliberate, scythe-like sweeps. At one point the machine started to tick like a Geiger counter. Eli could hear it. As the arc narrowed, the ticking became more urgent. At the optimum point his partner knelt to burrow into the sand with his fingers, sifting the sand carefully. Finally he got to his feet, holding up a small coin, which his partner acknowledged. The coin was dropped into a cloth bag and the process was repeated along the beach.

Eli stood fascinated, watching. Inside him a special alchemy was taking place . . . call it inspiration—revelation, even. An idea was forming, building itself to an explosion.

Some part of Eli's unconscious had, inevitably, heard the problem put to him by his assistant. This had nothing to do with its rejection by the conscious part of his mind. The subconscious could not be monitored by the conscious, subjected to value judgments, morals or ethics. The system had simply stored the information, and the sight of the two beachcombers had stimulated it, fitted itself into the complex matrix by resonating with the unique blend of his knowledge and experience.

A delighted smile was on his face. In that instant everything else was forgotten. Years seemed to have been sloughed off. He stood still for a moment, then ran, ran along the hard sand, retracing the path he had taken. Now on the softer sand, he stumbled once or twice. He ignored the exertion, that his heart was pounding in his chest. Normally the climb to the house would be taken in stages. Today he took it in one. He hurried directly to the garage, flung open the doors, backed his car out and speeded directly to the Center.

CHAPTER TWELVE

RICHARD JELKE, hurrying from the Clinic, arrived to find Eli in the control booth overlooking Connie's room, a room similar to those of the other two subjects. It seemed to him odd—unseemly, even—that the distinguished scientist should be unshaven, in damp sneakers, the cuffs of his scruffy khaki slacks also damp and salt-caked. Eli was so absorbed in studying EEG reports and tracings, his assistant's entrance went unnoticed.

Glancing down through the one-way window, Jelke saw her lying in a half-elevated position, her head encased in a turban-like bandage. A closer view would reveal the tiny antenna projecting from it. Connie appeared totally relaxed, even serene, her open eyes apparently seeing nothing, or so the neurologists who examined her regularly said. Each time Jelke viewed her, he was caught by her strange, even exotic beauty. Her fine features seemed even more delicate after her experience, and the flawless complexion more translucent. He found her truly fascinating, and the mystery of her didn't diminish the effect. The intercom to her room was open, and the only sound from below was the low pulse of the machinery pumping solutions to and from her body.

"Don't let her appearance deceive you," Eli said, startling him. "You're thinking how much more damage was done to her than to the others, who at least didn't need a support system."

"Without it, she'd die," Jelke said. "Except for her brain, I'd consider her dead now."

"Except for her brain," Eli repeated. "Her brain which persists in living. Except why do you forget she spoke in a language she had no previous knowledge of, no mean feat in itself? A dialogue. A conversation with someone unknown, am I right?"

Jelke said he was.

"And as we know, comatose, barely clinically alive patients rarely if ever do that," Eli said, adding, "all of which indicates a contradiction somewhere."

Eli now began one of his soliloquies for which he was known. A detached, remote look came over him, and it was as if one were eavesdroping into the workings of a splendid and unconventional mind.

What he said held Jelke. The technician at his console, listening as well, was no less fascinated. There had been moments in Jelke's association with Eli when he had experienced nagging doubts about the man's abilities; whether they could possibly match his reputation or was he a creation of public-relations puffery deliberately conceived to attract foundation funding. To be sure, these moments of cynicism were rare, but they did occur, most often at the operating table when he felt he could do almost as well. Almost. But there were also moments when he became distinctly aware of the man's special quality. Now was such a moment.

Eli was pointing out that the electrified microprobe

had grazed certain of Connie's brain neurons with devastating results. "If the trauma had been elsewhere—for example in Wernicke's area," he said, "she might simply have lost her speech, somewhere else her sight or her hearing, or her ability to move certain parts of her body. I, however, did considerable more damage. The entire circuitry of several systems was knocked out. It might have been an overload. The best analogy I can offer is a circuit-breaker cutting out."

"But why?" Jelke asked, suggesting it had apparently been the same with Tillie Harper and Floyd Gibbs.

Eli hesitated here. It was as if he was reluctant to express an idea—a theory—so . . . far out, as Tessa would say . . . that it was beyond acceptable science, entering the realm of metaphysics and philosophy where scientists were more reluctant to tread. It was controversial to be sure, maybe heresy, but he felt he had to at least give voice to it now. His extravagant theory, unproved, hungered for some confirmation . . .

"Nature is notoriously stingy in some ways. What she offers here, she takes from there, and I suppose it operates the other way around too. I could fall back on those ancient and disproved laws of matter conservation. Nothing is ever gone. Wasted. It merely changes." He turned to Jelke. "You follow?"

"Not in this context."

Eli took a step closer to the window and peered down at the immobile figure in the bed.

"What if in grazing certain of her brain cells we gave her a certain remarkable potential . . . a capability. But in her acquiring it, nature exacted its price. Maintaining the balance, as it were. It happened to Floyd. It happened to Tillie. Now we see it's happened to her. All three are, as you call it, comatose, yet all three are capable of exhibiting rare"—he hesitated with the word—"gifts."

"And her gift?"

"That's the question, isn't it? The precise nature of it. Was it a random episode or a repeatable phenomena? Repeatable and controllable. It depends on that, wouldn't you say?"

Jelke nodded.

"Then suppose we find out what we have," Eli said. "Now."

The neuroanatomists, the biochemists and various other specialists in their own modalities were busy at their tasks in the littered lab in the adjacent building. A few looked up from their benches as Eli and Jelke entered. They were puzzled by Eli's unusual appearance. Things were going on, they were aware. Gossip and speculations were inevitable in an organization of this nature, particularly since most were even kept in the dark about the details of the program itself. It was the difference between pure and applied research. They saw bits, pieces to do with their specialties, but very few were privy to the full mosaic of their work.

Standing at the threshold of the large lab, Eli said to Jelke, "Pick any one. It doesn't matter who."

Jelke indicated a young neuroanatomist who had been engaged in the dissection of the dorsal surface of the abdominal ganglion of a snail called Aplysia.

"Lew," Eli called out. When the mystified young lab man approached, Eli asked if he would accompany them. He then crossed to his office. The candidate hesitated. Eli, turning at the threshold, called back, "Come along."

The door shut, closing the three off from the rest of the curious staff. Eli dragged a chair to the center of the small, littered room. His movements were quick, purposeful. Telling the anatomist to be seated, he went about preparing a simple pendulum, attaching a small brass weight that he had taken from a delicate scale to a carefully measured length of monofilament. Crossing to the young man, he now held the pendulum suspended over his head. Jelke looked on, thoroughly mystified. For several moments nothing happened. Then slowly, imperceptibly at first, the pendulum began to move. Back and forth, back and forth. Its arc increased with each swing with a vigor that appeared independent of the man holding the end of the cord.

"Dick, get a paper and describe the arc span," Eli ordered.

When this was done as accurately as possible, Eli then requested the time of each sweep to be calculated. Eli, putting aside the pendulum, brought the computations to a small terminal hooked into the clinic's computer. Sitting in front of the keyboard, he tapped out the data into the device. Jelke stood behind him, watching the fluorescent read-out screen. Eli pressed a sequence of keys, and at once a blank graph appeared on the screen. Another key punched and a series of intersecting lines came up. Eli carefully noted down the precise points of intersection.

Switching off the terminal, he went to a shelf of books. Selecting a thin volume, he returned to the now totally confused young man still seated in the chair.

"Lew, please don't think me crazy," Eli said, "but I want you to follow my instructions exactly." He then explained that the volume he had selected was a copy of *Alice in Wonderland*, which he occasionally would read as diversion. He handed it to Jelke and asked him to open it to any page. Jelke selected the very beginning. With a felt pen Eli underscored a passage. He then handed the book to the man in the chair. "Now listen carefully," he said. "Very carefully. When that telephone rings once—just once—you're to read the underscored passage."

"When the phone rings—"

"Once. And as you read, concentrate hard on what you're reading."

"Aloud? Do I read aloud?"

Eli considered this a moment. "No, it shouldn't be necessary. But your concentration is. Is it all clear?"

The man nodded, looked at Jelke. Eli, ordering Jelke to follow, left the office. During the brief walk back to the adjacent building, Jelke found it difficult to keep up with Eli. At one point he heard a word that *sounded* like "dowsing."

"Did you say 'dowsing'?"

Eli stopped. He looked at his assistant, surprised he was even there. "Yes," and he nodded vigorously.

Back in the control booth, Jelke stood by watching as Eli had the technician at the console carefully adjust his rheostat to a frequency suggested by the computations he had made. Jelke was then told to stand by the phone and at Eli's signal to dial his office and to hang up after the first ring.

Eli, satisfied that everything was properly set and everyone understood his instructions, then stationed himself at the window to look down at Connie.

"Everything ready?"

The technician said it was.

"Dick?"

"Yes, sir."

"Two-millisecond pulses and hold it at that."

"Yes, sir."

"Recording equipment, tape camera."

"On."

"Then—begin."

The technician threw the toggle. For a moment the room was still. The men looking down could see no change in the woman below. They knew that a small charge of electricity was going through her brain, but there was no apparent effect.

"Dick, dial two oh eight."

Jelke had difficulty taking his eyes off Connie. With

nervous fingers, he dialed the three numbers.

"Just one ring," Eli reminded him.

Jelke listened a moment, then broke the connection.

All eyes were fixed now on Connie below. For a while there was no discernible change. Then, hardly distinguishable at first, a slight color suffused her waxen features. A relaxation was apparent. Her mouth slowly opened once. Twice. A vitality came into her opened eyes. The men in the control booth watched transfixed as she began to speak. Her words were at first undistinguishable, but the voice . . . the voice was unmistakably —a man's. The voice of a young man:

> "Alice! A childish story take
> And with a gentle hand—"

The voice sounded almost mechanical, empty of emotion, and the words were said as if by rote:

> "Lay it where childhood dreams are twined
> in Memory's mystic band,
> Like pilgrims' withered—"

"Enough," Eli said.

The technician cut off the vitalizing current, and Connie instantly returned to the shadows of her new existence.

Eli and Jelke sat in the small snack room of the Center. Both were taken up by their own thoughts, attempting to digest the events of the past hour. Eli looked down to the pattern of concentric circles he was making with his plastic cup on the slightly damp surface of the Formica tabletop. He was delighting in the high he was feeling, the high every experimental scientist seeks but only rarely knows. It was those first few moments when a new idea . . . or new application of an old idea . . . has its exciting confirmation.

Jelke was in no such euphoric state. His thoughts were confusion. He was involved in trying to fit things together. Connie's "episode" had baffled the best minds of the Center. Elias Nunn had come, characteristically theatrical, and once again justified his reputation by not only duplicating the phenomenon but explaining it. The explanation, however, was what was troubling him. It was clear that the subject had not once, but twice exhibited a gift of ESP, extrasensory perception, as a result of cortical stimulation; ESP, though, was not something he could easily swallow. It was the toy, the plaything of kooks and weirdos. One really didn't take such things seriously. It was for dark-of-the-moon rites and rituals. One man—only one man in this whole complex could even breathe the words *extrasensory perception* and get away with it. Elias Nunn. And could even he?

"You had mentioned the word *dowsing,*" Jelke said, unable to restrain himself any longer.

Eli looked up from the table at him. The pain and weariness were gone, like a beach washed clean by an incoming tide.

"And you're thinking," Eli said, "what business has such nonsense here?"

Jelke nodded.

"We're so clever, so brilliant, so superior to everything that doesn't come within our empirical paradigms."

"She exhibited—"

"What, Richard?"

He seemed to have difficulty even saying it. "Clairvoyant powers."

"*Nonsense,*" Eli said with exaggerated horror. "What are you saying? Merely waving a pendulum over Lew's head—"

Jelke quickly realized Eli was twitting him. "Please," he said with some irritation, "I'm confused enough."

"Because you've never been taught this at school? Some stuffed shirt like me never lectured you about it, or showed it to you in the course of rounds?"

Jelke chose to ignore the heavy irony. "You performed a CS," he said. "Somehow—accidentally—you established a new circuitry in the cortex. It happened with Tillie. It happened with Floyd. Connie Keenan has apparently been . . . blessed . . . with a form of clairvoyance."

"Q.E.D.," Eli said. "And blessed or not remains to be seen."

"The pendulum established a connection—a resonating frequency between her and the person whose frequency it was . . . am I correct? That's the dowsing principle, isn't it?"

Eli looked at the young man in front of him. He saw himself at that age, at that point in his career. It was all created for his presence in it, he believes, Eli thought, reflecting on his own youth. He thinks he fits, belongs in it . . . The words of Abraham Maslow came to him, words to do with three dominant appetites: security, sex and self-esteem. All producing their own brand of irrational behavior with perhaps the last creating more havoc than the others. And we're scientists to boot. Members of that elite. Privileged. We know the answers to all there is to know.

"Very good, Richard," he now said, smiling. "You've presented the facts."

"I've heard of dowsing with willow rods."

"A pendulum does as well."

"But I thought dowsing has to do with water?"

"Anything," Eli said. "Even thoughts, emotions." He mentioned literature on the subject that he had come across among his eclectic readings to divert him from the orthodox, obligatory tomes of establishment science and its "facts." "The man's name was . . . Thomas Lethbridge, an Englishman. Dowsing was his field and he suggested that the relationship between mind and body is electrical, that everything has a force field surrounding it . . . the force field that dowsers sense . . ." He went on to quote another authority . . . "Abbe Mermet. He said thought waves can travel around the earth at the speed of light, and it's as easy to dowse over tremendous distances as in one's backyard."

Jelke's voice was low. "*Mind* dowsing . . . ?"

"I've heard it also called mind-reach," Eli said, "and it may relate to a Professor Charles Richet's theory of crytesthesia, which accepts hidden perceptions, or as others say, second sight."

Jelke felt almost giddy. The foundations of his belief system were being undermined by a man he hugely respected. Not just a man—any man—but a superstar of science was giving these almost profane unscientific heresies credence, credibility.

Eli felt a moment's sympathy. He had been that young once. "You're upset," he said, "and I can understand it. I've desecrated your temple."

"I don't question what I've observed—"

"And observation fulfills empirical demands, right?"

"The implications—"

"Ah, implications. Dowsing, after all, isn't an accredited modality. So what are we to do with our observations which have upset our house? We've proof, that damned proof . . ."

"We can repeat it, I guess," Jelke said, offering the impression he was afraid they could, and also afraid they couldn't.

Eli began to talk about another scientist, "a young busy-tailed character called Sagan who said something to the effect that science is less fact than a way of thinking.

174

And what about Einstein?" he went on. "How far did he get with his suggestion that the distinction between past, present and future is only a stubborn illusion?" He sat silent a moment before continuing. "Will the pillars of our establishment accept our proof? How do we ram it home? Make the truth acceptable? Do you want to be part of it, Richard?"

"Of course," he said almost automatically. "The truth is—"

"Truth is a sometime thing that requires the qualities of a saint and a mystic."

"You taught me to believe that a scientist has a commitment to truth."

Eli nodded. "It does. As long as truth is wherever and whatever our discoveries and imagination take us to." He was already visualizing the scientific community. "ESP, clairvoyance . . . I wonder how far we'll get with it. We'll be called fakes, frauds, charlatans, exponents of eastern hocus-pocus."

"Your back-up authorities—"

"Like Gurdjieff? Like Ouspensky? That lot who believe that when we say we know something to be true we know nothing? People who say, don't trust your senses, there's more, much more beyond them, our senses lie . . . Authorities, Dick? Even if we—the two of us—accept them as authorities, what happens to our own belief systems? Do you surrender them that easily?"

"Are they incompatible?"

"Don't you think so? Are you surrendering what you've learned—what's been drummed into you? Are you giving it all up?"

Jelke was becoming confused again . . . the pillars of his tradition were indeed trembling . . . the years of training and conditioning in chemistry, physics, in the so-called inviolate laws of the universe were being questioned, coming unstuck . . .

"Think twice about it, Richard. You're at a crossroad. Follow me and you'll stand in peril—"

"Of losing my faith?" Jelke smiled uncertainly.

"I'm a known unconformist. A card-carrying rebel who's shaken up things more than once. But somehow I've managed to score enough points to get away with it. I'm the *enfant terrible*. Tolerated. They think twice before taking me on. But you? I'm not sure about you—"

"I can handle it so long as I'm on good ground."

"Good ground," Eli murmured. "What's good ground, I don't know." He studied the young man across from him. "As some of my less than ardent admirers will not be surprised to hear, I've browsed through the literature of the occult, the supernatural. Mostly as entertainment, out of curiosity. A diversion. I found some of it whimsical, charming even. But never serious. After all, I was dealing with freaks, nuts, believers in flying saucers and the like. To believe in it was to go Hari Krishna."

"And now?"

"And now how can I think that way any longer? They are the ones who've made a special claim on the higher emotional energies. They say there are those who have unlimited reservoirs of this energy, and can hook into it as our lady did a few moments ago."

Jelke hesitated . . . "It's a quantum dose to accept, all right."

"And can you?"

Jelke avoided the question, saying instead, "How often you've said we've only scratched the brain's potential . . ." Jelke allowed himself a smile.

"What is it?" Eli said.

"A ridiculous—maybe an absurd idea."

"After today," Eli said, "what's ridiculous? Absurd?"

"What if," Jelke tentatively said, "despite the coma, the lack of neurological response except for the brain activity, our patient is very much alive?"

Eli neither laughed, smiled nor deprecated the remark in any way. "And why not?" he said. "How large is the next step to the principle of multiple selves? The hierarchy of levels of existence? The so-called cosmic ladder?"

"Jung," Jelke said, almost reluctantly.

"Yes. Carl Jung, who said that the unconscious mind can be even more knowledgeable than the brain—"

An off-duty nurse entered the small room with its banks of vending machines. She seemed unaware of the men at the table. They watched in fascination as the coins she dropped in appropriate slots set wheels in motions, gears humming so that in a moment hot coffee poured itself into a cup, automatically followed by a dash of cream. A true miracle, Eli thought as he watched her leave.

"Our work's cut out for us, Richard," Eli said. "Keep your calendar free indefinitely."

"I thought our work was done."

"We've hardly scratched the surface. We're going to disprove everything we think we know or believe we have seen. We'll assume it never happened, could never happen. In other words, our working premise will be we were deceived. Our senses lied. We heard, we saw nothing. Our powers of observation betrayed us—"

"I don't understand."

"When I rise to say, 'Gentlemen, here it is.' When Miss Keenan is presented to the scientific world, let's be sure no one murmurs a doubt, whisper, even thinks the word 'fake.' To be sure, though, the inference will be that we are. Can you just see them swallowing this?" he added with a wry smile.

"And if she repeats—succeeds in proving her power?"

Eli's eyes turned to his assistant, taking on a distant look. "Then we may see interesting events."

Jelke wondered if he didn't detect a note of foreboding.

CHAPTER THIRTEEN

PITA BREAD, dolma and black olives washed down with retsina wine was Phil's dinner. It was the night of his brush with the two hit men, and now he was in a beach community some miles away. He had hitched a ride from a pair of surfers in an old pickup, riding in the rear beneath a canopy of elaborately painted surfboards.

"Heavy," one youth had commented, eyeing the heavier than usual traffic of law-enforcement vehicles traveling the freeway and parked at strategic spots.

"After illegals," the other had said.

Fearful of search, a cellophane packet of Hawaiian Gold had been scattered to the wind. Phil didn't mention that he was certain the search was probably for him. A final joint had been rolled and passed around as they had headed north, careful not to exceed the speed limit.

The café was called The Piraeus, and it was a place the aficionados came for a night of *hasipico* and *syrtos* dancing. *Oopas* and *yiasus* rang out. The jukebox played the

179

old songs of the Aegean and one or two from Yugoslavia and even Israel. The dancers ranged from expert to indifferent, but no one cared. Spirits were high and a warmth was shared. Except for the owner and a waiter or two, few were Greek, but that too didn't matter. Something of the mountain music—the flute, reaching back to the ancient *aulos* together with the harp-like *magadis*—evoking those ripened memories of other times, and for a moment or two the dancers felt at least as brothers, if not lovers.

Phil was sitting at a table far to the rear, his back against a primitive wall mural of the island of Hydra set in the bluest of seas. From this vantage point, he could see all who entered, and he watched carefully. It was his first meal that day and he ate ravenously. At one point he glanced at his watch. Ten hours more, before he could phone Angie as he was instructed.

What dream was he dreaming? What nightmare delirium was he in? It was all strange to him, this scene. This music. He had to prod himself. Convince himself he was living something real. A woman, a *patient*, for God's sake . . . he had fallen in love with her, against all his old codes and structures . . . and now she was in a serious danger that he really didn't understand. He should at least be trying to reach her, and here he was eating black olives and involved in a spectacle better suited to New York's Central Park meadow on an ethnic Sunday.

"Dance?"

He looked up. A sunburnt girl with yellow hair in faded jeans smiled down at him. At the moment, he didn't realize she was barefoot. "You look lonely."

Glancing toward the group acrobatics, he said, "I don't know how."

"I'll show you. It's nothing."

Awkward, self-conscious, he felt all feet as he tried to manage a *hasopersiviko* without falling on his face. He never thought of himself as a dancer. Even at the old 54 or the other discos to which he'd occasionally let himself be dragged, he'd tried to maintain an observer status.

Something in the ambience, whether it was the wall mural, which in a coffee shop at his own Little Italy might have been of the Bay of Naples with a smoking Vesuvio, or the music and dancing, he was reminded of the San Gennaro *festa* held annually on his own street in lower Manhattan. The tenements hidden as something grim and shameful behind the gay bunting of well-lit street booths peddling *sfinge* and *savolardi* and other pungent delicacies. Phil recalled the view from his roof ... the multicolored lights that festooned the great trellis beneath which it was all happening, and he would hurry down for the climactic moment when the effigy of San Gennaro himself would be carried down into the street from the church on the shoulders of the honored ones. The rich brocades and silks of the saint, smiling his benediction and made to look like a ragamuffin by the coat of currency pinned to him. Indulgences. Each dollar a forgiveness for a small sin or a solicited favor, larger denominations for larger requests. And the evening breeze that made San Genaro's green coat seem a living thing.

"Oopa!" the dancers cried out, and lighthearted, more daring now in his steps, he ventured an "oopa" himself.

"Phil . . ."

He stopped short, startled. He looked about. Despite the music, the laughter, the general clamor, he had heard his name. He couldn't be certain from what direction it had come.

The girl's hand groped for his to continue the dance. He ignored it. She shrugged and danced off. Anxiously, he looked around him. The voice, he was certain, had been Connie's, but she certainly was nowhere in sight.

Slipping from the hall, he felt himself drawn across

the oceanfront avenue, finding himself on the beach's soft sand. He walked into the darkness of the moonless night toward the ocean. Soon he was beyond the glow of the street lights. He pushed on. The supports of a lifeguard station rose spectrally before him. Skirting it, he came to the hard sand at the water's edge. He could hear the surf, glowing beyond with greenish phosphorescence. He stood still now. Listening. More than listening. Surrendering himself to whatever it was demanding his attention. His involvement. He let go. He allowed himself to become one with whatever it was out there. And all the while, he knew, he felt positive it held the key to hearing that voice again. Connie . . .

And then he decided he hadn't actually *heard* Connie . . . that it was something beyond the all-knowing—and knowing nothing—five senses. He held tight to this baffling notion, as if not to believe it would be forfeiting it —and her—forever. He was all the more desperate since he suspected . . . he wasn't sure why . . . that this could be the only contact they would have. A frail, most ephemeral of holds . . . tips of fingers touching as a quicksand seemed to be claiming her . . .

His mother's devoutness had pretty well soured him on any orthodoxy, although by rite of passage he considered himself Catholic. On a gut level he thought of himself as generous by thinking of himself as an agnostic. At least he kept his opinions and doubts to himself as compared to his father and brother, who came out with it: priests were to be tolerated at baptisms, weddings and last rites only. All else, as Angie would put it to his wife's horror, was bullshit. She'd cross herself on such occasions and mutter a "Hail Mary" so valuable points would not be taken away and the family would wind up together in heaven. . . .

So this moment for Phil was especially moving . . . shattering. It wasn't in his life-style, his ken—the super-

natural didn't fit the matrix of his scientific conditioning. And yet, here, this was *happening*. Connie's voice
. . . her presence . . .

The seasonal morning fog hung like a heavy, somber
drape over the area. The sharp metallic cries of gulls and
terns feeding on refuse washed up by the tide enhanced
the foreboding mood. Phil woke up in the rear seat of an
old abandoned Plymouth he had found in a small parking lot. He climbed out, feeling stiff and miserable. He
had slept little and was grateful both for the dawn and
the zero visibility.

The 7-Eleven store proved a blessing since even at this
early hour he could purchase a few toilet articles he put
to use in the restroom of an all-night coffee shop on the
Coast Highway. He still had forty minutes to call Angie,
and no forty minutes ever seemed longer. The waitress
refilled his coffee cup time and again. . . .

At the second ring, Angie answered. Phil was impatient. For the first time, he was aware just how tense he
was.

"What have you found out?" he asked sharply.

"Easy, brother. Easy. You okay?"

"I'm okay." He repeated his question, his anxiety even
more sharp-edged.

Angie told him how the senator had flown in to New
York the day before. "He's a friend, no question. He
dropped everything."

"Go on."

"I met him at the airport so I could fill him in on the
ride back."

"Where did you go?"

"First to that Doctor Ephraim's on Park Avenue. He
turned out to be in Zurich or somewhere. A convention.
These guys go on more conventions—"

"His nurse—"

"She never heard of your Miss Constance Keenan."
Phil could hear the careful tone, Angie's effort not to say
what he was thinking. "I told her to go to the files, make
sure—"

"And?"

"And she did. And came up with nothing. Kay, Kel-
sey, but no Keenan." The detective pointed out that he
couldn't go to the files himself since he had no warrant.
"She got sticky."

"Was she telling the truth, Angie? You'd know."

A pause. "I don't know."

"The senator was with you?"

"We went from there to the uptown hospital, where
we saw the superintendent."

"Wechsler."

"Yeah."

Again Phil was aware of his brother's hesitation. "Go
on."

"The lady was never a patient there. I saw the girl in
his office punch out the request for information on their
computer. I made her repeat it three times. 'More data,'
it said. Then, 'Unknown.' "

By now Phil felt like he was living out a Kafkaesque
nightmare. The normal, the understandable, the truth
from anywhere would have startled him . . . unreality
was becoming real, the outrageous to be expected. From
the phone booth he could see out to the parking area.
The fog had lifted somewhere, and cars and trailer rigs,
headlights on, where ghostlike, appearing and slipping
back into the thick grayness everywhere. Everywhere,
he thought. Inside him too . . .

"On the ride back downtown the senator said they
were lying," Angie was now saying. "All of them."

"Lying." It was as if some lifeline had been tossed to
him.

184

"You asked before. About that Ephraim's nurse, I mean. I said I wasn't sure."

"You are now? They were *lying,* right . . . ?"

"I'd say so."

'Say so then, for Christ's sake."

For some reason, Angie now changed the subject. "He was quite a guy, your friend the senator."

Was. *Was?* Phil picked up on it at once.

"Angie—"

The words that followed seemed flat, unfeeling . . . a police officer, resisting emotional involvement, making a report. Angie explained that he'd driven the senator to his apartment house, which he described as "one of those two-apartments-to-a-floor." He went on to say that a neighbor returning home that night from the theater had noticed the senator's door ajar. Peering in, he saw it. He called the police from his own apartment. "The call came at twelve-eighteen and the responding officers found the occupant 'deceased and lying between two beds in the bedroom.' "

". . . How?"

"The cause of death was attributed to suffocation. His own necktie. The coroner's report hasn't been filed yet."

Phil was no longer listening to details about a missing wallet, certain other articles of value. "The senator's wife was in Washington at the time. The assumption was that it was a homicide during the commission of a burglary. He happened to walk in on it."

"Angie, I don't believe it—"

Angie told him that the house had had similar recent incidents of burglaries. "I checked it out myself, it looked professional to me. Except for one thing."

"What's that?"

"Someone may have wanted it to look that way."

CHAPTER FOURTEEN

Hours—days—there was no respite in searching out possible weaknesses—even a single flaw in Connie's unique legacy. Never in Eli's long career had a project ever been subjected to harsher criteria, more rigid empirical examination. Experiments were endlessly, so it seemed, repeated under the most fastidiously controlled doubleblind conditions.

"What's going on? What's happening?" Kondorf wanted to know. He was finding himself angry and frustrated by the wall of secrecy thrown up at the Center. I'm no longer in control here, he thought miserably, but kept that to himself.

To reach Eli by phone was impossible, and once, unable to control himself, he stormed into the Center, getting as far as the nurses' second-floor station. There, coming up against the posted security, he insisted on seeing Eli.

"I'm supposed to be running this place" he shouted as Eli finally appeared.

"And you are, Norville. Who else would be? . . . Now listen, you'll be the first to get a special preview of everything when and if—"

"When and if *what?*"

"Miss Keenan lives up to expectations."

"Expectations!"

"Yes."

"And what may those expectations be?"

Eli patiently told him that there was now a slight reason to at least hope that the program's purpose might be realized. "And the moment it is, Norville, I can assure you, you'll be the first to know. However, I won't go off half-cocked. We need to stand on firm ground. Every claim must stand up. As you know, this is how I do things."

Kondorf looked at him grimly, then, without a word, turned and left the building.

Kondorf sat at his very neat desk staring at the phone. Now he reached for it to place a series of calls to various dependable informants he had strategically placed about the Institute; but these offered him little more information than he already knew: *something* was going on at the Center.

Each call added to his frustration, and with the last—almost as a reflex action—he grasped his wrist and timed his pulse rate. "Stay cool, idiot," he told himself. 'Lie back. Breathe deeply. There, that's it."

Heart type A, that he knew he was. He assessed his present state. Poison. Absolute life-threatening poison was how he saw it. He reflected on the envy he saw often in subordinates' eyes. He had made an art of concealing his fears, showing only a cultivated poise. If they only knew, he grimly thought, how it really was up in the ego-sphere of success . . . the cost, the pain . . .

Buzzing his secretary to say he wasn't to be disturbed he loosened his collar and swiveled his chair about to gaze out at the serene sea. He fixed his attention on a distant channel buoy, a mere pinpoint he used for his meditation exercises when his day-to-day problems threatened to overwhelm him.

No use. He could only wonder how he had allowed this to happen to himself. What a damn fool he'd been. He had deluded himself into believing he was in control of that crazy man he'd linked his life to. He had elected to ride herd on that mountainous ego whose unpredictable, outrageous postures vacillated moment to moment. What conceit he was guilty of. What vanity. If ever the penalty of *hubris* was just, here was it. Director? What director? Who was directing whom? Right now he felt himself at the end of a Snap-the-Whip. Hanging on during the Big Monster ride. The Cyclone. The Thunderbolt. Hanging on, clutching at whatever there was to clutch. And always there in the background like some ominous shadow was Washington. The Committee. Those cool, apparently unflappable bureaucrats he'd never met and from whom he could expect no mercy should there be a single foul-up. One misstep. Let Elias Nunn cause them a moment's displeasure or embarrassment and . . . the prospect of the program's failure was too awful to contemplate. He could only recall the expression "twisting in the wind," and he knew who would be doing the twisting.

He swiveled his chair about, reached into a drawer. "Damn those stoppers," he thought as he pressed and twisted the cap to the bottle of Valium.

It was a silk foulard scarf given to him by a Professor Alberto Salvatori of the University of Rome. It wasn't a new scarf, but actually part of the distinguished scientist's wardrobe. Eli had been a guest of the professor during a symposium, and the marble floors of his host's villa on the Via Flamenia combined with the usual January dampness and chill kept him constantly cold. He had somehow left the country with one of the professor's scarves, which now became the center of still another experiment.

The scarf was now being subjected to the pendulum treatment, since it had been worn by the professor at one time or another and presumably had absorbed something of his bio-energy. With the aid of the computer, Jelke established the wavelength frequency of its former owner after proper allowance was made for any possible "contamination" by Eli's use of it. The computerized data was brought to the control booth overlooking Connie's room.

The bed was gone now since it was thought the subject had recovered sufficiently from the operation's trauma. Someone had gotten the ingenious idea of providing a plain, wooden rocking chair. To everyone's amazement, she began rocking despite the fact she remained hooked up to the support systems. She rocked in a precise rhythm, never varying. The word "comatose" was never again used in referring to her, even though she responded to no stimuli. . . .

Connie herself had fleeting moments of lucidity. Thoughts, insights, flashed in her head like strobe lights. She could even make judgments. The entire process could only be compared to the brief parting of a curtain, a rent in a fabric. In effect, it was as though she were standing aside, eavesdropping on the existence she had left.

When a thin cushion had been added to the chair, she thought, How nice of them. They want my ass to be comfy.

She rocked. Back and forth. Endlessly. Someone said it was to her pulse, her induced breathing. The less literal-minded thought there was some connection to the sea beyond her window. No one went beyond that in speculation. She had been dressed in a yellow housedress. Felt slippers covered her bare feet.

One morning the matronly nurse tied little pink ribbons to her wig after the bandage about her head had been removed, and she submitted to it as she did to everything else.

"For Sunday," Nurse Chatterton said.

I'm the star dummy, Connie thought. Gussyin' me up. Maybe they'll stick me in some window. The Easter special. The observation was fleeting, immeasurable in time since there was neither space nor time in her dimensionless universe . . . Like looking at the world through the bottom of a broken beer bottle, she once thought. Shadows, people—people, shadows. Here, there, running around so. Shadows of shadows trying so very hard to believe they're more.

Her most constant companion was the technician she sensed rather than perceived beyond the one-way glass window. Such arbitrary obstacles: time—distance—these man-made contrivances meant nothing to her. She knew all there was to know about him, as she did about others; and the remarkable thing was she didn't think of her perceptions as remarkable . . . When it isn't golf, his mind's on cunt, she speculated. Hole-orientated, that's what he is. One kind or another. As if I don't know he's gotten it off more than once in front of a centerfold. The son of a bitch is playing with the idea of sneaking down here some night to slip it to me as if I were some pneumatic dummy from a porno shop. I only hope he doesn't louse up my tubes. Tubes, ha-ha. Who will he make me into? Bo Derek? His wife—if she only knew the roles she's played, she'd claim an Oscar. . . .

Eli and Richard Jelke made their computations and the technician fine-tuned his console controls accordingly. Eli glanced at the wall clock. It read twelve-fourteen. "Which makes it roughly nine P.M. in Rome," he calculated.

"Ready?" he asked the technician.

"Yes, sir."

The three men in the small room looked down to the woman below.

Here it comes, she thought with sardonic amusement. Another one. It's such a big deal, they can't accept it. If they only knew. Oh, Phil, Phil, where are you? Keep your heart—your mind— open. Let me come through—

"Now," Eli said, and the toggle switch closed the circuit allowing the microvoltage to beam out to the antenna barely protruding from beneath the wig.

Connie's rocking stopped instantly. The body relaxation followed. There were the facial changes. Her mouth opening once or twice, and in a moment a man's voice coming from it.

"Filetto di bue Toscano . . . Braciola di Maiale . . . Scottadito d'Abbacchio . . ." The voice was flat. Emotionless. Not unlike a train dispatcher at an Italian terminal, except Eli recognized the words not as places but as foods.

"Have you got him?" Eli anxiously called across to Richard Jelke at the telephone.

"They're trying to reach him."

"Petto di Tacchino . . . petto di pollo con panna e funghi . . ." On went the recitation.

"Got him!" Jelke announced. Eli hurried to the phone after ordering the technician to maintain the cortical stimulation.

"Alberto," he said into the instrument. A brief conversation followed in Eli's poor Italian. In a few moments the call was ended.

"Well?" Jelke had come up beside him, his anxiety apparent.

"My very puzzled friend, Professor Salvatori, is at this moment in a very fine restaurant on the Piazza Navone. I've been there myself. He was called to the phone just as he was considering the menu." Eli turned to order the transmission to Connie cut off. Looking back to Jelke, he said, "Should we be convinced?"

"What more can we do?"

Eli shook his head slowly. Nothing. It was done.

It was time, Eli reluctantly decided, to bring the director of the program into the well-guarded secret. He realized it would be the beginning of a new phase, and yet it couldn't be avoided. The program wasn't his, he was merely its caretaker, its guide. He recognized the ambivalence in him. There was the needed recognition of his achievement. The program had been a seed thrown into the wind. It had sprouted and taken root. The fruit of the investment could now almost be tasted.

The intercom buzzed in Norville Kondorf's office. When told it was Elias Nunn he became alert.

"It's time, Norville," Eli said. "Time for you to come in on it."

"Now?"

"Now, and for you only." Eli then asked the director to bring to the Center something that belonged to him or was handled by someone else—someone preferably in some far corner of the world. Kondorf was confused; Eli had to repeat the instructions.

The year before, Kondorf had taken a photo safari—his wife had said it would be *wonderful*—through the Lake Tanganyika section of southeast Africa. In his office was a souvenir of the jaunt, a so-called primitive mask made by a Ruanda craftsman. It was this that he uneasily carried to the control booth, where he found Eli and his assistant.

"Will this do?" he asked.

The mask was a rather crudely painted affair of wood, hemp and small cowrie shells.

"Excellent," Eli said, accepting the mask. He asked

some questions ... was it modern? ... was the craftsman still alive? ...

Kondorf shrugged. "As far as I know."

"Well, we'll see."

Kondorf watched the mystifying ritual of the pendulum suspended over the mask, then followed the computer calculations. Eli alerted the technician at the console.

"Come over here, Norville. Stand at the window and keep your eyes on the subject down there. You understand the intercom is open." Eli gave further instructions to the console-man. "Watch now, Norville." Eli nudged the technician, who had already adjusted the rheostats to a precisely calibrated flow of shortwave broadcast that would be received by the antenna in Connie's brain. The technician threw the toggle switch.

The director leaned forward, startled. The woman he had seen only as a waxen figure rocking herself by some mechanism which seemed apart from her, now abruptly stopped the motion. It was as if some unseen hand grasped the chair. Her face went through subtle changes ... a life of sorts came into it, her mouth opened slowly, then shut, then opened once more, but now a voice came from it. A man's voice. Guttural. Rapid. One word flowing into the next so that it seemed one continuous stream of sound. Connie Keenan, born on the North Shore of Long Island and raised there for the most part, was, now, speaking fluent Swahili.

The words were incomprehensible to Kondorf, and to the others, and yet the director had the conviction that he was hearing a language associated with the mask. He managed to turn his head away from the spectacle of the woman below to stare at the mask. He then turned to Eli, who was watching him.

"That's ..." Kondorf began.

"... the voice of the tribesman who made your mask,"

Eli said. "It's what he's thinking or saying aloud to someone at this very moment—"

"Aw, but that's—"

"Impossible, yes." Eli then ordered the technician to cut off the current. Connie's expression went empty. Her rocking resumed.

"If this is possible . . ." Kondorf began. For some reason, he turned to Jelke, as if he would find confirmation there. His expression suggested he was being made the butt of a heavy-handed joke. A look of cunning suspicion came over him.

"Like the brain itself," Jelke said, "cortical stimulation holds endless surprises."

"Norville, have you considered the implications?" Eli said. "Tillie Harper's music is at least music, Floyd keeps our mathematicians reaching. But consider what you've just seen. The consequences."

The director was still unable to digest what he had seen and heard. "It was . . . real?"

"It wasn't a parlor trick, I assure you," Eli said. He understood the shock, the resistance. Eli had his pride, God knew, and it may indeed have gone before the fall, but he was also recalling Robert Oppenheimer's first words after viewing the Alamogordo test: "We now know sin," and he wondered in some deeper part of himself if he too was about to turn loose some awful force on the world with the profound potential for *both* good and bad. "Think . . . consider what it can mean," he said, "to know the innermost thoughts and utterances of anyone in the world at any given moment."

Kondorf considered it and found it perfect. The incalculable dividends . . . to know motives, read the most devious minds . . . to be able to supervise words, contracts, treaties . . . to enter into the most secret of meetings, cabals. It was, in a word—power. Untold, uncomprehended power . . .

The morning mists lifted according to their seasonal schedule, and the day became bright and sunny. Phil had been offered a ride south by a middle-aged couple who had had breakfast in the same coffee shop he did. Their 1969 Buick never exceeded the posted speed limit, and snatches of their conversation drifted back to where he sat preoccupied with his thoughts.

How could it have happened?, he wondered. The day before, beginning with its violence and ending with Greek music, and, for God's sake, his dancing to it. All right, these could be accepted, but the business on the beach was too much. That, he decided now in the glare of a new day on a busy freeway, could only be explained by his anxiety for Connie. The idea of communing with her? Pure hysterical conversion, he thought, or some such psycho-pshymicho . . .

The old people's questions were politely insistent. Of course he had been offered the ride out of goodness of heart, he realized, but then there was also something else. It was their need for other company. To hear each other's voices, impressions and opinions other than which they could anticipate from each other. For all these years . . .

"Our name's Nelson. I'm Wilbur."

"Martha," Martha Nelson added.

Phil felt he had to offer his. He now did something deliberate, out of a need for *some* confirmation. If someone could believe some small part of what had happened to him, maybe he could accept the whole of it. And yet he knew how it would be received . . .

"My name's Doctor Carlino," he said, almost casually. "I'm a brain surgeon. From New York . . ." Almost at once he could sense the chill. The old man adjusted his Green Bay Packers peaked cap against the sun, which had broken through the morning mist. His foot at the same moment felt for the tire iron he kept close to the seat.

Phil went on, "I've lost a patient. Not in the sense we doctors say we've lost a patient. I mean, I've lost a patient, and I'm here trying to find her again." He told them, speaking faster, that she had a possible cancer in her head. "And you know, of course, that that can be very bad."

Wilbur Nelson kept the tremor from his voice as he tried to change the subject. "Would you believe it," he said, "if I told you how much we've saved usin' regular 'stead of that ethyl like the manual says we should use?"

"We're Michigan," Martha Nelson said for no apparent reason other than her own sudden uneasiness. "Upper Michigan. Ever hear of Judge Voelken? One of ours, wrote *Anatomy of a Murder* . . ."

"Lake country. Bass," Wilbur Nelson added.

Phil said . . . "That's interesting . . . I've never been to Michigan . . . Did you ever lose someone close to you . . . then dream about them? Feel they've come back to you? I mean, really come back . . . Do you have to be religious to feel that? My people were Catholic, I don't suppose you're Catholic. No."

"There! Look at that!" Wilbur Nelson called out. "Another police car, Martha. Did you ever see so many police cars?"

Phil kept silent. So did Martha and Wilbur Nelson. Phil hadn't meant to be so carried away. He turned his thoughts to Angie, who had told him to sit tight. Do nothing. But he had to do *something* . . .

A head-on approach at the Institute would have been foolhardy, he decided. Who would he see? Who would he ask for? The very least that could happen would be he might further endanger Connie. The idea of confronting

Elias Nunn himself occurred to him. Yes, why not? He'd know some answers and he'd surely be beyond any of the violence . . . well, wouldn't he? Phil knew of his reputation, that vaunted nobility. The man would be outraged, he decided. The very least he would offer would be an inquiry. After all, they were colleagues . . .

He approached the large house on the bluff with caution, particularly after he had spotted the stakeout of cars and men. Putting his early street training as well as his Vietnam experience to good use, he was able to skirt the premises undetected.

The only access to the property, he decided, was by way of the bluff going down to the beach. The climb down was no less difficult than the one up; eventually, however, he found himself on the terrace near the swimming pool.

Glancing down at his torn clothes, realizing he hadn't shaved in twenty-four hours, he imagined the greeting he would receive if he presented himself cold. The recent experience with the old couple was fresh in his mind; his general appearance was nothing to reassure anyone. The Nelsons had been absolutely terrorized until they had finally unloaded him.

Aware that the front door would put him in view of the watch at the gate, he found a terrace door unlatched. Cautiously sliding it back, he entered the gracious living room.

Rosarita, the housekeeper, happened to enter the room at that moment. Crossing herself automatically, she fell back; then, recovering her composure, she burst into rapid-fire Spanish which his Italian and years of service at the New York clinic helped him at least partly to decipher. She would call the police who surrounded the house . . .

He tried to make her understand he was there just to see the doctor, not to steal or hurt anyone.

"What do you want of him?" a woman's incisive voice said almost directly behind him.

He turned. It was Tessa, her face cold and hostile.

"I've no appointment with him, but—"

"He doesn't do his business here," she interrupted. She turned quickly toward the housekeeper, who was stealthily making her way toward the terrace doors. "*No*," Tessa said. "Rosarita, stop."

Phil understood at once. The housekeeper was on the point of calling the police. What was more important, the young woman didn't want that. He also perceived a certain hostility between the two women. The Chicano woman finally turned, her stolid figure erect in its dignity, and, rather haughtily, left the room.

"Thanks."

"What do you want with my husband?"

Husband? He was surprised somehow, even though he had a vague awareness of the eminent neurosurgeon's colorful reputation. Well, she'd been decent and trusting, she deserved his confidence . . . He launched into a shortened account of his bizarre reasons for being there, telling all that had happened in spite of the fact he was aware how bizarre it sounded. To his amazement, she showed no surprise. She didn't say a word. Her mouth had become a thin line and her eyes took on a rather sad look. Feeling more assured, his words came more easily, ending with the . . . mental visitation with Connie. Why push the credibility of it all?, he thought.

"Come with me," she said.

He followed her to the large hall off which the other rooms opened. At a closed door, she turned.

"This is his study," she said.

He was baffled by her tone, her manner. Why was she bringing him here? Why did she accept what he had said so easily? He felt a certain nervousness standing before the portal of the great man's inner sanctum. For a moment he thought of the ideas generated here, the papers no doubt written. Well, forget it . . . no time for being awestruck at the inner sanctum.

Tessa opened the door, and he went in.

He was totally unprepared for what he saw. The devastation—the havoc spared nothing but the furniture itself. Not a shelf—not a wall spared. The lamp was overturned and the refectory table which had served as a desk held a litter of torn and jumbled papers. The scene was the aftermath of some awful destructiveness.

He turned to her. His shocked look was question enough.

"Come in," she said. He followed uneasily. She then, as if she were a museum's docent, launched into an unemotional description of the room.

"On this wall were diplomas from an assortment of universities, doctorates, y'know. Right here was a photo with the Swedish king taken at the Nobel ceremony. The plaque was here. The document, whatever you call it, here. Not the check though. Oh, not the check." Her laugh was too loud. "Now here," she went on, "were various pictures. A whole assortment. A Who's Who in the world of science. Every country. Every nation." She continued the litany of honors, awards. At the table she said, "And God knows how many articles, papers and books were done here." Abruptly she stopped and looked at Phil as if seeing him for the first time. "What did you say your patient's name was?"

"Constance Keenan."

"Yes." Her look became remote, she seemed to drift off.

"What about her?" he said.

"You'd like to know where she is."

"Yes."

"It's so very simple, you know—"

"What?"

"What's happened to her is what happened to the others."

He felt himself losing patience. "What others?"

"The zombies, doctor. The ones they keep in that zoo called the Elias Nunn Center for Behavioral Studies."

He stared at her, and she met his stare. What was this incredible thing he was hearing? Comprehension—certainly acceptance—was beyond him. He could only think the woman was a flake. Off the wall. And yet . . . something in him realized . . . some logic saw the pieces begin to fit . . .

"I'm sorry," she was saying, "it's just how it is. It's what he's about these days. My husband. People are somehow made available for him, the idea being that genius can be created, don't ask me how exactly. You're a doctor, you said. A neurosurgeon, like him?"

"Yes."

"Then the words 'cortical stimulation' should mean something to you. Do they?"

"I'm not sure—"

"Well, it's his thing, a thing he does well, I suppose. But then, he's Elias Nunn, a genius in his own right, right?"

"Excuse me, you're not making too much sense—"

"I've *told* you," she said angrily. "He makes—he *creates* —genius. I've seen it, actually, I mean. There's something I don't understand. What happens to the . . . subjects . . . it apparently becomes unimportant. People, people like you, me. The doctors, the nurses, I mean, no one seems to care."

His eyes moved to the savaged wall.

"Yes," she went on, and as if reading his thoughts, went closer to the wall, ran her fingers over it. "A very important, a very fine man, so says everyone. The Pope even. Here was where the picture of Eli and the Pope was. The Pope, imagine." She shook her head. "Vicar of

Christ, if he knew." She now began to intone the names of places . . . "Oak Ridge, Birmingham, Washington. There was that place that little fish was threatened by the building of a damn. It was called an endangered species." She looked strangely at Phil. "As if we're not, people I mean." She moved to a cabinet, flung open a drawer and riffled through papers. "Here's where the social and political activities are filed. Causes, you know. Where the saint documents his credits."

He came to her and gently took her into his arms. He'd recognized the edge of a breakdown. She looked up at him. There were no tears in her eyes, just hurt.

"I'm sorry," she said. "About your friend, I mean. God, I really am . . ."

CHAPTER FIFTEEN

SHE SAT serenely rocking, indifferent to what she already knew since past, present and future held little differentiation. Time-warp blurred all distinctions; and even if it hadn't, the grand scheme of things of which she was now a part made mundane affairs picayune and absurd.

Soon there'll be a great fuss over me, she thought during one of her moments of involvement. Even greater than now. Without bitterness, she thought about her past life, its raffish search for acknowledgment of a kind. Well, now, here, she had it, more than she cared for. I'm soon to be the so-called eye of the storm. Front-page stuff. If not 60 Minutes, *I'll make the* National Enquirer *yet . . .*

It was just after the demonstration staged for the Institute's director, after she had returned to her interminable rocking.

Eli, seeing how he had shaken up the man, had said, "Go on, let them know. Let it begin."

And begin it did.

Telling his secretary he wasn't to be disturbed, Kondorf reached into a lower desk drawer and drew from it the red telephone with its special voice-scrambling device—a direct line to Washington.

After what seemed an interminable eighteen minutes, all five men were gathered at their respective phones. They listened to his account of what he had witnessed without interruption. With characteristic cunning, he was careful to give assurance that Elias Nunn himself had conducted and vouched for the phenomenon.

"It has his seal of approval and I've no reason to doubt that the woman can reach out anywhere with her mind by some process we'll shortly understand," he continued. "It's incredible—truly incredible, listening as she tells you what someone is saying or thinking." He spoke proudly, as if the accomplishment was mainly his, an attitude he would settle into.

The Committee, five highly intelligent men with a grasp of conceptual ideas, suppressed their skepticism in acknowledging the importance of such an extraordinary achievement. They could evaluate its potential perhaps even better than Kondorf or Eli himself, in terms of practical application. There was no doubt that they took it seriously, if for no other reason than that they had access to CIA reports on Soviet activities in the field.

One said, "How soon can it be demonstrated for us?"

"Anytime you wish," was Kondorf's reply. His fears and anxieties had vanished. "We really pulled it off, gentlemen. We can all be proud."

He waited for an affirmation; instead he heard the voice of the committee chairman, a voice which he at once recognized, respected and even feared, in spite of its deceptive gentleness. So disarming in its affability, shy almost, that one had to strain to pick up what the man was saying. Kondorf listened attentively.

"Norville," the voice said, "what about that New York doctor we hear is in your area?"

Kondorf's heart skipped. He fought to sound casual. "Oh, yes, that matter's being followed up."

No one asked if anything had gone wrong, why the matter was taking so long. The silence, though, said that and more.

"Followed up?"

"The breakthrough at the Center diverted our attention momentarily, as you can understand," Kondorf said brightly. "You can imagine our excitement, but I mean—"

"Unfortunate," the chairman interrupted.

"I beg your pardon?"

"It's unfortunate, I said," was the even-toned reply, "since the doctor apparently had had the opportunity to make a telephone call to New York, to his brother, who it turns out, is a detective."

"But—"

"I'm not finished, Norville. What is even more unsettling to us is that the call was made from Doctor Nunn's house."

A pause. Kondorf didn't have to ask how this was known. He often suspected his own telephones were bugged. Not a word now from the six men on the single conference call. But accusation fairly crackled over the line. Kondorf didn't need it spelled out. The success of the program, ironically, made the situation worse.

"I can assure you," he said as firmly as he could, "he hasn't made contact with Dr. Nunn—"

"How do you know that?" someone asked.

"Because our resident genius has been just that—in residence here at the Center." He went on to explain that Eli had not been home in days. "That's the nature of the man. His concentration. He's become tunnel-visioned."

He realized that to suggest that Eli and his wife were estranged would beg the question—why. And to respond to that would open a whole new can of worms that could only put him in a poor light.

The gentle-voiced inquisitor persisted in his questioning. "The conversation the doctor had with his brother suggests he's aware of the program," he said. "Did you know that, Norville?"

"And he was highly upset," another said.

"He couldn't know about this latest thing you've mentioned, could he?"

"God, no," Kondorf quickly said. "That would be impossible, absolutely impossible . . ."

Another committee member: "Our sources advise us," he said, "the detective has made contact with a certain investigative journalist."

As the voices gained momentum, the questioning sharper, Kondorf felt cornered. He also got the sense that these frightening men were frightened, remembering the not so distant hounding by press, Senate committees and a public concern about Washington hanky-panky.

"We were on the point of calling you" . . . "It's becoming untidy" . . . "What's she to do with this New York fellow . . . ?"

Kondorf explained that Eli and his wife had been having trouble for some time. "There's that age difference," he told them. "You may have seen her recently, you can understand . . . her needs . . . For the time being we're keeping her where she is, not that she has credibility anywhere, still, especially with this latest, new development, we can't afford chances, that must be perfectly clear." He was talking rapidly now. Convincingly, he hoped. "Maybe it's just as well they're together, that doctor and her . . . at some future point a final resolution will be that much easier—"

"Future point?" someone asked.

"For the moment, I'd leave them be."

"Why?"

"I've given up predicting how our unstable maverick will react to anything," he said, adding, "least of all to something to do with his wife. Right now he's essential here. Let me repeat—essential."

For several moments there was silence on the line. No one had questioned the words "final resolution," what they implied. There was no apparent concern, even. They were playing a game of the highest stakes. A game plan was needed. One with set pieces. Output would be determined by input, and factors such as morality became irrelevant.

The five men now put together such a plan. It was a first but essential move to safeguard the program. Kondorf listened attentively; he was forbidden to take notes. He was not to get in the way. His function would be to follow up, attend to loose ends. The scheme was as dramatic as it was daring, and could only be done with the resources of government. Kondorf knew better than to point out the risks. He was aware of the greater risks in not launching the operation.

"Good God," Eli said when Kondorf told him what was to happen. "This is the most foolish cover-up since Watergate—"

"Not at all," the director said. "It's, in fact, brilliant."

"Brilliant?"

"Since the program obviously hinges on our subject, shouldn't our first consideration be her security?"

Eli suddenly became aware of his deep weariness. The days, the nights, the tugging and pulling of his personal problems, not the least of which was his troublesome ambivalence, even though he had become adroit at rationalizing it.

"Security against *what?*" he said.

"When they speak of naive eggheads, they must have had you in mind, Eli. Have you the slightest idea of her value? The competition she represents? What do you suppose their reaction would be if they suspected what we've pulled off?"

"They—?"

"The Kremlin, every capital and chancellory in the world . . . friends, enemies alike. When they become aware of her existence, they have a choice of three imperatives—duplicate her, destroy her or steal her."

The effect on Eli was unforeseen, especially by himself. Kondorf's warning evoked, brought to the surface, what had been simmering for days now, without his full or even partial awareness. A bond between himself and the woman had been slowly building. Realizing it was a shock. Its unnaturalness frightened him less than the realization he was the active element, she the passive one. And if it were so, it then had to be because of a need in himself, he realized. An unfulfilled need, which she served. . . .

It was hours later. Dusk was coming on and the sea in the distance lost its color like a fish flopping on a deck. The purple of the evening sky grew even deeper, and the night which came on proved moonless, a boon to the men involved in Operation Limbo.

A convoy of canvas-covered trucks from the nearby Marine base rumbled through the Center's sentry gates. MPs quietly lined them up behind the buildings. The silent efficiency of each man's movements suggested a commando operation. Men sprang from vehicles and scurried inside the building. Other men unloaded quantities of materials. Officers emerged from a staff car and were met by the Institute's engineers carrying rolls of blueprints. These all gathered about a large table in a lower-floor office. Floor plans were spread out and studied. Aides transmitted instructions by way of a short-wave radio.

As Connie sat rocking, oblivious of the unusual activity going on close by, Eli stood in front of her, regarding her. The small spotlight in the otherwise darkened room focused on her, giving her an eerie theatrical effect.

So I wonder what *is* this happening between us?, he thought. Am I some sort of Pygmalion who reversed the process by transforming a beautiful creature into clay?

Pygmalion! What's this Pygmalion crap, she thought, picking up instantly on his thoughts. You see me as someone that says you're Mr. Wonderful . . . otherwise you've got big troubles, old man . . .

I don't even think of Tessa, he was thinking, with some astonishment. This one has replaced her. Wiped her from my mind. Established her priority. This goddess—did I say goddess? Well, she certainly looks like a goddess. As a goddess should look. Can anything so lovely be—nothing?

Moving closer, he touched her hand, resting on the arm of her chair. It was warm. The warmth of it shocked him more than if it had been cold as marble, or death.

The headlights of the rented Plymouth followed the winding road to the well-lit house. Angie Carlino was puzzled. Phil had said that the house was staked out. Guarded. He could see no signs of it. Neither man nor vehicle was spotted as they drove up, and their entrance through the gate went unchallenged. Beside him in the car was Herb Spector, a *Daily News* reporter who rated a byline on his stories. He was a friend of Angie's through the years of the city's hurly-burly, and if it were possible to imagine a more cynical character than Angie, it would have had to be Herb Spector. . . .

A meeting had been arranged in a dimly lit Third Avenue saloon, hanging onto its traditions by sheer grit. Each time another of his regulars passed on, the owner, Sam Moore, felt the perfumed, hot breath of a faggy boutique or posh eaterie anxious for the property.

After Angie had told his story, Herb Spector had leaned over the mahogany bar to peer straight down into his Jamison's straight. "Shit," he commented. He knew the detective as one not much given to flights of fancy.

Angie's practice was to keep a long list of unpaid debts, figuratively speaking . . . running the gamut from sleazy underworld characters to some of the top shakers and movers of the city. It was his special m.o. "I'm a lazy sonofabitch," was his explanation. "This way I don't have to rely on brainwork." He had called in a marker, so to speak, that the reporter had owed him for some time for some small, almost forgotten favor. "I'll even personally pay your air fare," he had said, "and you'll thank me yet, Herb."

"California?"

"Yeah."

"It couldn't be Yonkers?" . . .

Sitting now in the Nunn living room of gay flowery chintz and gleaming copper, Phil told his story, Tessa hers. Neither was interrupted. "It's called CS," she was saying. "Cortical stimulation."

The newsman, Spector, squashed a chewed-up end of a never-lit cigar in the ashtray. "Psychosurgery is illegal," he said. "You ask me to believe there's such a government program, and that they knocked off a senator to keep it under wraps?"

"I don't know anything about a senator," Tessa said.

"Well, I know what happened to me," Phil added. "And what about Connie Keenan? Where is she? What's happened to her?"

Herb Spector looked closely at Phil. He had never met

the neurosurgeon before, although he knew of his reputation, and not just from his brother Angie.

"Phil, where are the men you said were out there?" Angie now asked.

"I don't *know.* I know a stakeout when I see one. You . . . pop—things rubbed off."

"Mrs. Nunn?" Angie said, turning to Tessa. She shook her head slowly. "It's just suddenly disappeared. Gone."

The room went silent. Doubt, skepticism soured the air. Phil looked at his brother, who was regarding his sausage fingers. He felt his anger boiling up.

At approximately that moment two men were having dinner at a seafood restaurant on the coast road just outside town. One was Arthur the chauffeur, no longer dressed in twill, his peaked cap nowhere in sight. The other was the survivor of the contract team sent from the East to deal with Phil. Large men, they ate heartily, washing down broiled swordfish with Michelob that they drank from the bottle. Mutual dislike and distrust lay thick between them.

"No way, I don' like it no way," the Easterner said, his dark, hawklike face tight with frustration.

"It's the way it is. Like it," the other said.

"He's a pigeon. A sittin' pigeon. He's mine any time I want him." The mob soldier wiped his thin lips delicately with a napkin before touching his jacket over his heart, as if finding strength, reassurance in the weapon he could feel there.

"Go home, I tell you. You'll get paid just like it was done. It's how it's to be."

"Who says?"

The chauffeur's look was somehow meaningful. "It's how it's to be," he repeated. "The contract's off but you'll be paid like I said."

"You don't unnerstan'—"

"I *understand*. You're a pro," the chauffeur said, appeasing. "You got pride. It's natural. The most natural thing. Honor."

"Pride, shit. Rafaelo's dead. My wife's sister's brother. What do I say to her she asks, 'How did he die? Where's the body? Was a mass said?' " He pushed his plate away in disgust.

"Fresh."

"What?"

"You said you don't eat frozen fish. I swear it's fresh."

The hit man's black eyes burned with the thought of a certain man dying. Only that could expunge the stain, the badness he felt. Not fresh fish.

"Don't do nothing," Arthur warned. "It's how it's wanted. Pass it by."

"Phil . . ."

That soft voice came again in his sleep, awakening him. He lay there motionless, not daring even to move. The room was dark, and from outside came the sawing of crickets and once or twice a night bird's lonely song.

Again he heard . . . *felt* it. "Phil . . ."

There was no actual voice, he now decided, *but* neither could he be convinced it wasn't real. Very real . . . The day before he had seen a hawk high up in the sky, hovering, then with hardly a movement gliding in lazy circles. He had thought idly at the time, was it in sheer joy of life, freedom, power to fly, or was it just its search for food? He thought of it now, again. How easily the simplest things could be misread. . . .

Her voice. *Her.* He recalled her image as he remembered it best. Moving . . . the way she walked with that bottled-up energy of a highbred racehorse. Impatient to be off somewhere. Was a single night together enough to cement this kind of bond? He'd never been a Romeo-Juliet believer, eternal love at first sight . . . yet here he was, taken over by the most profound feelings he'd ever known. That he was even capable of them was a kind of shocking revelation that defied questioning about such mundane considerations as why and how come.

She was . . . a presence, a presence that transcended description. Feeling her presence made him want more and more of her, and he tried to hang onto it as though his life . . . and hers . . . depended on it.

CHAPTER SIXTEEN

IT WAS called Operation Limbo for reasons having to do with more than the dark void to which Connie and the others had been consigned. The incredibly complex operation wouldn't have gotten off the ground without reams of printed orders and requisitions; inter-agency cooperation would have required memoranda signed, initialed and countersigned. All in all, to accomplish its ends in so short a time suggested a bureaucratic nightmare. But the impossible had been achieved; some would have called it a Washington first. In short, not one word —one hint—of the entire affair had been committed to paper. It happened, yet officially had never happened; no one could prove that it had. The operation simply flashed briefly: a super-Nova to vanish forever except in the memories of those involved. Connie had been secreted from the Center, as was Tillie Harper and Floyd Gibbs. The entire staff which attended them, knew anything about them, likewise vanished. And the facility showed no signs of having ever been used for the experimental purposes. Limbo.

The following morning the rented Plymouth and an Orange County deputy's car pulled up in front of the clinic building, parking in an area marked "forbidden." The occupants of the cars emerged, came together and marched up the few stone steps and through the automatic plate-glass doors. The party included Tessa, Phil, his brother Angie, Herb Spector, a uniformed deputy and a clean-cut, well-dressed young man proudly conscious of the fact he had recently been chosen as an assistant district attorney. He carried in his pocket two documents, one a writ of habeas corpus and another a search warrant, both properly executed and signed by a local judge. These had required considerable effort and running about by Angie and Herb Spector, who realized that without the documents their investigation couldn't have begun.

Norville Kondorf was in form. This was his forte, dissembling. He handled the situation with Byzantine flair and the proper blend of elegant aloofness and patience. In an offhand remark to the young attorney, he made it clear that dealing with the mental stress of the aggrieved was one of his responsibilities. It wasn't said but clearly implied that personal loss was often followed by pathetic, often desperate delusions. Glancing at the documents presented to him, he tossed them across his desk as he would so much trash mail.

The young assistant district attorney had little taste for the mission, but couldn't avoid it. He knew all too well the political clout of the Institute throughout the area, and here he was serving papers on its director. The situation was an embarrassment. It was certainly no way to launch a career fresh out of law school, carrying hot potatoes for Easterners. A cop and a reporter no less, and neither with any official sanction. As a racing sailor by avocation, he knew before leaving his office he would be trimming sails and tacking cautiously, if not deceptively.

Kondorf had flashed at him his toothiest smile, making it clear he understood and sympathized with his unpleasant duty. Once or twice he glanced quizzically at Tessa with a look that suggested . . . poor child, up to more mischief with your personal problems . . .

Phil was guarded in his approach to the director. He knew the type well—the tailoring, the hair-styling, the Bally loafers and general life-style which usually included a late-model Porsche or Mercedes, more often than not leased. Now he said, "Could we have a look at the place where Doctor Nunn works?"

"By all *means,*" Kondorf said, getting to his feet.

Tessa stopped short—dumbfounded. What had been the sentry house with two uniformed guards was no longer here. It had disappeared. She looked about, confused. How could she be mistaken? Where there had been a steel meshed fence topped with barbed wire there was now a row of oleander bushes, full with pink and white blossoms. And people were coming and going about their usual business.

Phil asked, "What's wrong?"

She shook her head. Nothing. She turned to look at the director, who was in casual conversation with the two locals about next season's chances for the Chargers with better quarterback protection.

Angelo Carlino and Herb Spector drew up the rear. Walking silently, they peered about like field dogs searching for a scent. But nothing seemed unusual, out of place. There wasn't a breath of tension in the place. What was even more disturbing, it had nothing to do with the woman's description. At one point Angie had said to her, "How many times you been here?"

"Once—twice," she corrected.

"Day? Night?"

"Once in the daytime."

He made a wry expression. A young woman, a technician in a white tunic, was passing. In a few quick steps, he caught up to her.

"I beg your pardon, miss."

"Yes?"

"There used to be a fence around here?" he said. "And a gate house about there."

She looked at him oddly and hurried off.

They were in front of the low building now, and Kondorf turned to address them. "We keep this place separate from the Clinic for reasons you'll understand," he said, adding he hoped they had a stomach for what they were to see.

The Elias Nunn Center for Behavioral Studies had been artfully disguised and camouflaged. It had become an entire new facility. The modality was now for drug and alcohol addiction, and the place had become a place for treatment and research into associated problems. Patients' rooms had been filled with pathetic characters in various stages of withdrawal and therapy, the control booths altered, their equipment dismantled and removed. What it had previously been was ingeniously disguised; not a single clue was left to suggest its former use.

The director was an enthusiastic tour guide, expounding on the features of the facility, anxious to impress.

Both floors were visited. People who worked there were questioned, rooms, charts were examined. Patients talked to. Phil looked into cabinets, checking on medications. Angie and Herb Spector touched walls, even testing for wet paint.

"Did I dream it?" Tessa wondered. Her confusion at least mitigated some of her embarrassment.

"This is wrong, all *wrong*," she finally said to Phil, who

218

patted her hand comfortingly. He knew what a credibility crisis was. He was feeling he was a sort of partner with her.

At one point, she ran up to Kondorf, in conversation with the young assistant district attorney, demanding, "Where's my husband? Where is he—?"

"If you don't know—"

"*Tell* me."

He smiled his smile. "Trouble again between you, eh?"

"I asked a question."

"He mentioned a symposium somewhere. The brain and linguistic competences, or something of the sort. I'm not his keeper, you know, and he doesn't consult me on everything."

Angie said, "Let's see his office."

That room in the adjacent building had been carefully scoured of anything incriminating. No notes, papers, anything to do with cortical stimulation, were anywhere in sight. Otherwise, it had been left as Eli himself had left it. Angie and Herb Spector had seen the havoc done in the study at the house. The relative order of the office suggested that the destructive orgy might have been done by someone other than Eli. It did Tessa's cause no good in the detective's eyes. He had seen the overkill frenzy of certain women under stress, and his thoughts were running in that direction.

"What about Constance Keenan?" Phil looked directly into Kondorf's eyes. There was no reflex, no flinching.

"Constance—"

"Keenan."

"The name on the writ," Angie added.

Kondorf made it clear he didn't know who she was, that he had never heard the name. "Now, gentlemen," he concluded, "I do have other things to do—"

He started to turn away, but Phil, holding himself in

check too long, grabbed at the man and swung him about. Grasping him by the broad lapels of his elegant jacket, he shook him fiercely. "You are a goddamned liar—" and before the uniformed deputy could collect his wits and react Phil was slapping Kondorf with the palm and back of his hand.

The deputy, lurching forward, was about to hit Phil. Angie expertly deflected the blow, urging the man to cool it.

"He's a lying creep." Phil was shouting now.

"Shut up, Phil. Shut up," Angie told him, at the same time keeping the deputy from closing in. . . .

It was a sober, glum group sitting in the Clinic cafeteria. It was ten-thirty in the morning and between meals. The place was only moderately full, mainly with white-coated interns or technicians on coffee breaks. The busboys wiped tables and clattered the crockery and aluminum trays with unnecessary zeal to remind the loungers that others had work to do if they didn't.

"I asked for a Bialy," Herb Spector said. "They had no Bialy, they said. They never heard of a Bialy. I said, 'Give me a Danish then.' Angie, try some of my Danish."

Angie, understanding the thought behind the offer, said, "Thank you."

Angie had been sitting, brooding, avoiding looking at his brother, who had put him through this embarrassment, making him look like a schmuck, as he thought of it. The word was sure to get around. Herb felt sorry for Angie. He knew how it was. He had family too.

"California Danish is like California pastrami. Shit!" he grumbled. "Tell me if I'm right, Angie," he said, pushing the plate across the table.

Angie broke off a piece and put it into his mouth. The other three, their minds on other things, watched intently as the man slowly chewed. The pronouncement finally came. "Yeah. It's shit, all right."

"Never make it, California," Herb Spector said ruefully.

"Never," Angie Carlino agreed.

Tessa seemed to be speculating aloud. "What I'm thinking is," she was saying, "we've just witnessed the classic literary cliché. The missing room."

Eyes fixed on her. She looked up to them.

"Yes," she repeated, "the missing room. I mean, the missing center and all its . . . contents."

Angie Carlino's face grew still darker. "What you coming down with now?" he growled. "Enough is enough."

"Angie, shut up," Phil said. *"Listen."*

"You listen," Angie said halfway out of his seat as he glared at his brother. Herb Spector reached out and pushed him back. "Angie, they run planes to New York regularly," he said. "Let's hurry an' get lucky." He turned to Phil to say, "Ask if anyone over there at the counter knows what celery tonic is."

It had been the night before when Operation Limbo had come off. The Center had been transformed. Kondorf hadn't thought it logistically possible, yet it had been effectively done.

He had led one small, select group to Connie's room for a crucial part of the exercise. Entering first, he had found Eli standing in front of her, silent and contemplative.

"Eli . . ." he had said gently.

Eli turned. "Yes, yes?" Kondorf saw the quick struggle to adjust to the present. There was a sound and Eli looked back at the waiting men. "Oh, yes," he now muttered.

Strangers, he thought with a sudden concern. New people. She was to be moved. The idea unsettled him. There'd be change. Would he lose control of her? What were they heading for? Where? What conditions would prevail for her complicated case? Disaster scenarios flashed in front of him as Kondorf gave a sign to the men. He watched apprehensively as the rocking chair with Connie in it was carefully hoisted aboard a dolly on wheels. One of the squad appeared to be having trouble with the support system connections. Eli rushed forward, pushing him aside.

"Not that way, you damn fool . . . let me do it . . ."

As Kondorf witnessed this erratic display, he felt uneasy. This won't do, he thought. It can't be left in his hands any longer. He was considering the enormous stakes involved. He thought of the work, the effort and money expended. My own future's totally committed, he decided; no, I don't like it. It's . . . unsound, unhealthy for everyone. Even her. Nevertheless, he put his hand on Eli's arm and smiled solicitiously. "She'll be all right, Eli. She'll be all right, I promise you."

It had been the director's plan to leave Richard Jelke behind, but at this moment he decided to change that. A standby was essential.

The area behind the building had an eerie quality. Beyond, in the distance was the clinic building with its lit windows, here and there the bright cobalt blue of a television set bolted to the ceiling of a patient's room. Here it had been all darkness and gloom, the shadowy silhouettes of the orderly line of vehicles of all sizes. Dark-coveralled Men had scurried about them to orders issued in low voices. Once or twice, when absolutely necessary, a low-beam flashlight would glimmer briefly.

Connie, attended by Eli, had been carried into a motor van painted black. As its side doors had slid shut, Kondorf looked about to see the other two subjects, Tillie Harper and Floyd Gibbs, lifted into separate vehicles.

The nearby beach had been dark except for the flickering red-and-white warning lights of a pair of Air Force CH-53s, helicopters known as the Super-Jolly-Greens. Their rotors had been kept spinning at idle, pulsing the air with a deep throb. It was an excitement strange to this desolate stretch of beach, mostly known for its nude bathing. The crews lounging in the gloom before the opened doors had been smoking cigarettes, making small talk. From time to time the officers would glance at the luminous dials of their watches and anxiously look back toward the mainland. It was the procession of dim lights that heralded the convoy's approach, at which time the men went into action to prepare for its arrival. At the convoy's head, two MPs had jumped from their jeep and, with luminous batons, guided the convoy down an especially prepared ramp to the beach itself.

The operation had concluded with the same precision. Tillie Harper and Floyd Gibbs, the latter sedated, had been loaded into one of the craft and attended by Richard Jelke. At the very last moment, Kondorf came aboard. Eli saw to the lifting of Connie into the other aircraft. When everything appeared in proper order, the officer on the beach flashed a signal to the pilots. Rotors accelerated, and amid a blinding sandstorm both craft lifted, circled once in steep banks, then flew in a direct course to a United States Air Force Space Defense Center in the remote mountains of Arizona. . . .

Glimpses of the operation had flitted in and out of her consciousness like hyperactive children in a playground, darting this way, that—in ever-moving, often purposeless patterns. I know how the Mona Lisa must have felt, she thought, as she was being lifted and carried from the building. All these nice young jocks who once would never have handled me so lovingly.

The attentions of Eli she put up with. Not that I have any choice in the matter, she thought. But he's hurting. Oh, yes, Phil's hurting. And the more attached he's becoming, the more he's hurting. I'm his love and his punishment all in one. Well, suffer, you sonofabitch, you got me here . . .

And her thoughts flew, literally, to Phil. Cleansed themselves there. And she knew peace again. . . .

CHAPTER SEVENTEEN

AN AREA not too distant from Flagstaff, Arizona, was as desolate, isolated an environment as was to be found anywhere. It was ideally suited to its denizens of rattlesnakes, scorpions and other creatures with—if not the good sense—the instinct to burrow down and away from the desert heat. Sagebrush and saguaro grew in sparse patches, eking out an existence from the inhospitable desert rimmed by purple mountains shimmering in the noonday heat. A single blacktop road, soft underfoot, ran in an unrelenting straight line across the desert floor, tantalizing the infrequent traveler with the mountains, which never seemed to come closer. Savage hordes of flies in a frenzy of feeding swarmed over lizards and other reptiles crushed on the road.

This was the only visible life in this land once shunned, even feared, by Indian tribes past. And this was the region selected by the Security Council to house a redundant space defense facility, deep inside one of its

225

mountains. It was the exact duplicate of the sophisticated complex located at Cherokee Mountain in Colorado, and in the event of a crisis could be activated at once.

For miles about the perimeter of the installation, a high fence and posted signs warned off trespassers; and the closer one approached the mountain, the more tight and sophisticated security became. The immediate access, hidden from the road, was guarded by camouflaged sentry posts, beyond which was the terminus of a small gauge railway leading into the mountain itself, at a grade which increased to ten degrees. The entrance itself was guarded by massive doors of steel-alloy, hung so delicately a man's weight could move them. A quarter of a mile inside and below the mountain, a series of chambers and passageways had been carved from the living rock; and here the personnel of the installation could function and sustain themselves comfortably for an indefinite period.

It had been the consensus of the committee in Washington that, if the program's chief hadn't lost his senses and gone off into peevish fantasy, then they had on their hands a resource of incalculable value, transcending by far the program's expectations. The President himself, apprised of the situation, was at first skeptical, as anyone would be, but at last, reluctantly, cautiously consented to go along, mainly perhaps because he did not dare not to.

Absolute secrecy was mandatory. Should a demonstration prove successful, a heavy lid of secrecy would have to be clamped down. Come a hint of Connie's existence, and countermeasures would cancel out her effectiveness in a flurry of panic in a world of animosities, distrust and special interests, where the best peace was stalemate and standoff. On the other hand, were she to prove no more than a scientist's fantasy, and the demonstration a failure —then the entire program, scrapped or not, had its potential for a devastating scandal. Many people were involved. A single defection, a careless word, could mean disaster of a major order. It had been recalled that the construction of the first atomic bomb, the Manhattan Project, had required security of this kind. To forestall media leakage, preparations were made to invoke the appeal of national security in the event exposure was threatened.

It had been seriously debated whether the subject should be housed at Fort Knox; logistics, however, ruled that out. A secure repository was nevertheless essential; the cavern at the root of the mountain had been selected as uniquely suitable, particularly since neither distance nor the permeability of her environment apparently mattered.

The largest of the chambers had been modified to accommodate Connie and the equipment necessary for her survival and functioning. The same staff which served her at the Center served her here; and there was Eli himself, who now dedicated himself to her with something of the fervor of a high priest serving an ancient oracle or goddess.

The analogy was appropriate, although the rough, granite walls of her chamber had been artfully disguised so that it would appear anything but a cavern, the end of a crude shaft inside a mountain. Instead of smoking torches, the lighting was fluorescent except for the spotlights which constantly held her in their beam. There were no sacrificial altars on which to pluck out animal organs and entrails for portents; that function was analagous to the electronic gear and other devices. Her robe, rather than of some handspun linen, was of a starkly simple but handsome caftan of pale blue silk cut by Halston, and her head was encased in a nylon wig instead of a bejeweled diadem. And lastly, she did not sit on a throne of gold or ivory, but on an old wooden rocking chair that Goodwill might have accepted. Still, the analogy held. Her role was akin to that of her classic counterpart—her knowledge of what transpired in the minds of men held the key to their future.

Eli trusted no one else even to approach her. His appearance took on that of a fierce, Old Testament patriarch. His temper shortened, and his mood turned irrascible. He ate his frugal meals at a small table in a far corner of the chamber. If a nurse or technician had to approach her for some reason, he stood by, watching closely, glowering, and more often than not taking over the chore himself. He seemed actually jealous that she could need anyone but himself. Gossip ran through the facility suggesting he had actually been heard to murmur endearments of some sort to the "subject."

Had he gone round the bend? The proverbial-cliché mad scientist? Only if obsession were madness—and obsession had been characteristic, if not essential, to his other achievements as well. Some people attributed his genius to it. Now perhaps, it was enhanced because of his rather bizarre involvement with the subject. . . .

Connie, too, perceived Eli's deteriorating condition, but felt no pity. No compassion. A good part of my life, she thought, men have jerked off inside me. That's all it was. No more. Played with the idea the connection was meaningful. Looking for something they lost, or never had but wanted. I'm still playing the role with you, huh? The ole receptacle role. But I tell you, mister, I feel toward you like I felt toward them. Nothing. Zero. Zilch. What's more, what have you paid me? A freebie. You're having a freebie on me, which has always been against my principles . . .

Day, night—they meant nothing in this place beneath the earth. There was a time for this, a time for that, and people did them accordingly. When it was time for his sleeping, he slept little. He had his small room assigned to him, but instead of retiring there, he would sprawl in a comfortable chair, his legs stretched out before him, and gaze across to where she sat, illuminated, sometimes rocking, sometimes not. There was no sound other than the hiss of the air conditioning, the mechanical, rhythmic thump of the support system and an ever so slight creak of the rocker. . . .

Oh, Christ, she once thought. I'd just as soon he didn't go bananas. So long as I hang onto what's left, which I'll soon enough shed, it might as well be him. No Barbie doll ever had a better mummy. She had come to regard him in that light, an old watchman hired to guard a ransacked, gutted property fenced in by old doors of many colors, experiences and comings and goings. So hang in there, doc, she thought. Warm yourself at the small fire left in me. . . .

The Committee's journey from Washington, D.C., aboard an Air Force plane had been a strangely silent one. Some were accompanied by aides and staff members, but the usual banter was somehow restrained. The importance of the journey had somehow dampened— put a pall over their spirits. At an Air Forces installation in New Mexico, they transferred to another CH5 helicopter for the final leg of the flight.

The vista of desert and mountains below depressed them, jarred their perspective. A few brief hours ago their cloistered egos had been intact. They had carpeted offices with many-buttoned phones, all the usual accoutrements of power. But now, somehow, it was flattening for them, becoming increasingly distant. Remote. Shrinking.

Kondorf greeted the party as it emerged from the aircraft on the camouflaged heliport. Hurrying them into the air-conditioned bus, he was still unsettled by his introduction to them. They had been voices on the phone, voices with unlimited powers blown to extravagant proportions by his own insecurities. Now he saw them as they were . . . mortals unsure and out of their environment.

He was aware of their nervousness as they entered the small railway car, which would carry them into the mountain. He recalled his own feelings at his entrance, and felt superior. An Air Force colonel in charge of the facility explained the details of the place, but he knew they were uninterested. The elevator ride still further down did little to reassure them. Kondorf made the announcement that the demonstration was scheduled for the following morning, after they had been briefed by Doctor Nunn himself.

At dinner in the mess hall Kondorf played the gracious host. It was all very first-rate, including the wines. The colonel cautiously explained it was the first time alcohol had ever been permitted at the facility. The food was no less impressive, even though Kondorf heard one of the Committee members say, "I didn't come to Arizona for a lousy prime rib."

"Where's Doctor Nunn?" someone asked.

The director explained that the scientist was busy with last-minute arrangements. "But he'll join us shortly," he added. "Meanwhile if you have any questions I'll be glad to answer them."

There were no questions.

The rec room with its pool table, Coke and pinball machines was as incongruous a place as could be imagined for their first encounter with Elias Nunn. The pin-ups on the wall behind the bar seemed frivolous, and even the green baize-covered table about which the group sat had been more accustomed to games of seven-card stud.

The five Committee members sat silently, self-consciously regarding the small, well-wrapped packages in front of them. These contained the bizarre request Kondorf had made—that they bring with them certain personal articles which had been in contact with someone in some far-off place.

Awaiting Eli, the tension grew. The prima donna was doing his act again, they felt. It did nothing to reassure them that they weren't on some wild, spurious adventure; and as the moments passed, their annoyance built. Kondorf had the good sense to say little. Calling attention to himself at that moment was the last thing he wanted. . . .

Eli entered the room with his characteristic flair, which commanded immediate attention. Kondorf was delighted to see that he had changed his clothes, cleaned up his act as he thought of it. This was the old Eli, the charisma intact.

Kondorf noted too that even as he entered, the others —almost involuntarily—got up from their seats. After the introductions and the men had resumed their seats, Eli stood looking down at them for several moments, studying each one in turn. Not a word was said, not a motion made. Kondorf had the very strong impression that a sort of battle of wills was going on, a silent competition for dominance. He didn't care too much for this, it could mean trouble.

"Eli," he said, lightly, "the Committee has been briefed in only the sketchiest way. The in-depth indoctrination should be from you, I felt."

The soft-voiced chairman spoke for the group. "We've been told what to expect, Doctor Nunn," he said, "but it's so unusual—so bizarre, you must admit—we would be especially interested in some explanation of the phenomenon. We are—if you will forgive us—*practical* men."

Eli's air since his entrance into the room had been that

of a distinguished professor entering a hall for his very first lecture to a green first-year class. There was that touch of condescension, that establishing of superiority.

"Mister Ludwig . . ." he said, addressing the chairman.

"Yes?"

"We did meet in Washington, but I'm afraid I can't recall your field of expertise."

The chairman's pink face became even pinker. His eyes behind the rimless spectacles narrowed and his thin lips all but disappeared. "Apart from being Committee chairman, I head a section in the Department of Energy—"

"A government career man?"

"I come from private industry."

"Ah. Congratulations."

Chairman Ludwig appeared about to lose his well-cultivated poise. But Eli's attention fixed now on the chairman's neighbor. "And you, Mister Drew?"

The thin Mr. Drew with a patrician face, Brooks Brothers school stripes to his tie, smiled wearily, and a little warily. "Doctor Nunn," he began, "with all respect, I don't see—"

Eli flashed his famous "laser look," as he said, "Tomorrow morning I will put you into an intimate relationship with my subject. I feel we're entitled to know certain things."

Kondorf was startled. The "*my* subject" struck him at once. He hoped it had gone by the others. What did he mean . . . "we're entitled to know"? Know what?

"Andrew Gallagher," the third Committee member announced, and got to his feet, his tone and manner belligerent. "I'm Assistant Secretary of Defense in charge of Intelligence and before that I was a colonel in the Marine Corps." He looked the role, with an almost bald head that seemed carved from granite. As he spoke the words as if he were on a drill field, his dislike for Eli seemed an almost palpable thing.

The other two Committee members were somewhat anticlimactic. Government career men, one in charge of a bureau at the Department of Commerce, the other a Treasury Department official.

When it was done, Eli's gaze swept the group. His expression appeared sad, disappointed. Slowly shaking his head, he said, "I was hoping at least one of you were involved in something more—"

"Such as?" Andy Gallagher said, still on his feet.

"Food resources, conservation, arms control . . . I confess I had the hope." He saw the dismal looks about him. "I know, it may sound hypocritical, considering my role in the program, but that's just the point. I'm looking for some—any—high purpose in your interest in my subject. So that we can rationalize its harm with a greater good to come from it. . . ." He turned to Kondorf. "You spoke about those things once, Norville. I'm not mistaken, am I?"

Kondorf rose slowly. "Yes, Eli. Yes. A great deal of good will come of it, I *assure* you."

Eli nodded and smiled bleakly. "Well, we meet tomorrow morning, gentlemen. And don't forget to bring your little packages that I see." . . .

The room was silent for several moments after he had left, but the chagrin—the grimness Kondorf saw about him—spoke loudly. "He's been working very hard, very hard," he murmured, then suggested they all retire. They'd be awakened for breakfast, after which would come the demonstration. His too cheery brightness was met with varying expressions of anger, resentment and frustration.

Andrew Gallagher remained in his seat after the others had left. He sat staring at the small, brown-paper-wrapped box in front of him, his bald head gleaming in the overhead fluorescent. Kondorf approached him.

"Mr. Gallagher?"

The Assistant Secretary of Defense didn't look up. "Sit down, Kondorf," he said.

Kondorf sat.

His eyes on the package, the ex-Marine said, "I can't tell you exactly how many lives were put in jeopardy getting what's inside that. I can't tell you because I don't know. I just know there were many. A whole network of operatives." He looked up at Kondorf. "Ask me," he continued. "Ask me what's inside. Go on."

"What's inside?"

"Hair."

"Hair?"

"The hair from the head of one Simeon Katlarsky. Hair cuttings from the barber he goes to in the Elizabethskaya section of Moscow, where he lives. Two days ago it was on the floor there. Now there it is. A car was wrecked outside, the barber and Katlarsky ran out, the operative in. Our problems had just begun. The hair had to be smuggled out, flown to East Germany, then to the west, then to me. A dozen—two dozen lives were put in danger. At least. It was done on the basis of your telephone call. Your message. The news. Nothing so good was expected, it's why I went all out."

"Mr. Gallagher—"

"Who is Simeon Katlarsky? Is that what you want to know?"

"Yes."

"An egghead. A scientist like that lunatic who was just in here. I don't know what he looks like. I don't care. I only know he happens to be the top gun in the Soviet research and development program equivalent to our ASAT."

"ASAT?"

"The anti-satellite program. Killer satellites, Doctor Kondorf."

Kondorf listened in near awe as the nature of a future war was explained to him. Cities, nations, populations wouldn't be decimated. Wiped out in a nuclear holocaust. "Not at first," Gallagher was saying. "Not unless some maniac politician runs the show. On either side. Someone who, for one reason or another, defies the inevitable fact."

"What's that?"

"That the next war will be won or lost in space. That whoever knocks out the other's communication satellites has won it flat out, then and there. Information won't be received in places like this to be relayed to the Pentagon, the President, the Security Council. Commands won't be issued. Missiles will sit in silos, subs . . . those that do get off will be exploded in space. Deaf, dumb and blind, that's what happens to the country who loses the ASAT competition. At which point you run up the white flag, lie down and say, 'Enough. We've had it.' And you have had it, because anything else is suicide."

Andrew Gallagher looked at his wristwatch, and as he studied it, said, "From our same operatives who got the hair, the survivors, we know that in one hour and twenty minutes there's going to be a Kremlin meeting. Top brass. Simeon Katlarsky will present the state of the art of their ASAT." He looked up to Kondorf. "One hour and twenty minutes," he intoned, his eyes holding the man's opposite him.

"What can I do?" Kondorf said weakly.

Gallagher leaned his thick body forward. "Elias Nunn is something off the wall," he said. "And frankly he's trouble. He always has been, hasn't he?"

The director nodded. His mouth was dry.

Gallagher consulted his watch again. "One hour and eighteen minutes," he said quietly. "Can you do it?"

"*Me?*"

"Then who?"

The switching on of the light in Richard Jelke's room had awakened him, the sight of the two men startling him further. Sitting on the edge of the bed, he had listened to what was asked of him. Unreal, he thought. The tiny room felt overcrowded, but he knew that wasn't what was suffocating him.

"You can do it," Andrew Gallagher said finally.

"I—I don't know."

"Dick, understand its importance," Kondorf said. "In view of Doctor Nunn's violently negative attitude—"

"He knows?" Jelke asked.

"And declined," Gallagher quickly lied. "You must know his politics."

Kondorf picked up the cue. "He has no right to speak for us in such matters. We're scientists, not politicians."

"He'd feel . . ." Jelke began weakly, feeling it was a betrayal of a man he revered.

"There's neither room nor time for personal feelings, doctor," the ex-Marine said quietly. "Consider down the line how you'll feel if you blow the opportunity. It'll come back to haunt you. Now, I've taken Doctor Kondorf's word the lady can deliver. If so, you're the one person on earth can save it." He paused here. The air conditioner hissed. Kondorf was about to say something but a small gesture from Gallagher stopped him. In a moment he continued, "We've little more than an hour before that Kremlin meeting."

Kondorf dismissed the technician monitoring the control panel and support system in Connie's chamber. The three men entered the room itself.

Andrew Gallagher, tough as he was, was awed by the

beautiful young woman rocking quietly in the chair across the chamber.

"Can I go closer?" he whispered to Kondorf.

"Yes."

Memories rose in Gallagher for some reason. Memories he had thought forgotten. Fishing with his father in the Minnesota lake country. At night the curtains of the aurora borealis. That time as a kid in Chicago. As a choirboy, he had somehow been locked in the choir loft overnight together with his friend Arnie. They had whispered the mysteries of what a woman must be like down there as they masturbated each other. Then came the lightning storm, and he had cried out in fear, and guilt. God had seen them! God had seen them! . . . Why did he think of such things now?, he wondered . . .

Jelke, aided by Kondorf, worked furiously. There was the analysis of the Russian's hair, then feeding the pendulum data into the computer.

Kondorf read the young man's concern as he glanced from time to time toward the heavy metal doors which remained open.

"If you're worried about Doctor Nunn," he said, "don't. He's exhausted and sleeping well."

Eli was indeed sleeping.

Walking back from the rec room along the whitewashed corridor with its complex of exposed pipes and cables, he had been reminded of the countless interconnecting subterranean tunnels beneath countless hospitals where he had worked at one time or another. These by contrast, he knew, had to do with the distribution of mass death in one form or another throughout the world.

Would he permit the demonstration?, he had asked himself, struggling with still another dilemma. But how could he not? After all, in the final analysis, it would fulfill his promises for the program. As an alternative, he had shrewdly considered strategies by which he could have the scientific recognition of the achievement yet limit the uses they inevitably would demand of her. What if, instead of keeping the secret, he himself exposed it? Made it known to press and public? A swell of protest, especially among young people . . . Washington and the consortium of multinationals would be slowed down or stopped . . . thinking on such exciting possibilities, he had lain down on the narrow bed in his small room to think them out—

He woke up abruptly, sat up erect, listening. He heard nothing but the slight sound of the air conditioner, yet he had a distinct feeling of unease, something very amiss. His thoughts went at once to Connie.

Turning the door handle, he found it locked. He struggled with it a moment, then banged, kicked at the door. Calling out brought no response either. He reached for a chair and smashed it several times against the sturdy door.

A young man's voice came to him. "Doctor Nunn. I've orders you're to stay put until morning. I'm sorry, sir."

Eli moved from the door to sit on the edge of the bed. *Déjà vu,* he was thinking. He had seen this happen before. A scientist had spoken his conscience and had suffered for it. Now that the program could maintain itself by others, he'd become superfluous. Redundant. A nuisance, in fact, if not a threat.

He reached into a pocket for his thin black cigarettes. Lighting one, he was about to blow out the match when the idea came to him . . .

Air Force MP Corporal Clyde Hangstrom, in helmet, brassard and wearing a sidearm, had been posted outside the scientist's door. Leaning against the opposite wall of the narrow corridor, he was planning his own strategy. Twice he had blown his salary on that Flora with the big tits whose father ran the Flagstaff Buick agency. The disco, the booze and grass took it all, and she wouldn't even let him touch her. Head was okay, she said, she'd give him head once, but no more. He had shown her the box of rubbers, she still said no. A finger, just touch it a li'l—no! Should he try it—invest in one more date?

It was then that Corporal Hangstrom first saw the smoke curling lazily up from the door sill. His reaction was swift. Unlocking the door, he threw it open. The room was filled with smoke. Running in was the last thing he remembered as the sharp blow caught him at a nerve center near the side of the neck.

Richard Jelke made what he thought was the proper rheostat adjustment at the console. Gallagher had meanwhile summoned the interpreter he had brought with him to come at once to the chamber without mentioning it to anyone. This was a plumpish, dark-haired young woman who wore heavy spectacles. She entered, ill at ease and nervous. Gallagher provided against her freezing up by getting Kondorf's assurance that all that was said and done in the room would automatically be recorded on tape. Gallagher again consulted his watch.

"We've two minutes," he said.

"How will we know if the meeting is canceled for some reason?" Kondorf said.

"We won't."

"Are they punctual?"

"With top brass there, they'll be punctual."

"I'm ready," Jelke called from across the chamber.

Gallagher stationed his interpreter as close as possible to the young woman rocking in the chair.

"Go on, go *on,*" he urged, as he felt the squeamish woman resisting his pressure. "She won't hurt you. And relax, for God's sake."

Gallagher didn't consider himself a superstitious, or even a religious man. He prided himself on his toughness; yet he too couldn't shake off his uneasiness. It wasn't just that he felt himself in the presence of something beyond the known, the natural . . . after all, he also was defying the committee by striking out on his own this way. He knew there'd be hell to pay . . . but the risk had to be taken, the prize was worth it. Nothing could be more important than what he had to learn, and depending on that flaky egghead who already was raising his pink flag could screw things up for sure . . .

Kondorf nodded a signal to Jelke, who flicked the toggle switch. The reaction came as expected. Connie's rocking stopped instantly and the fixed expression on the pale, lovely face became something else as her mouth opened once or twice soundlessly, as if flexing itself. Then came the words. Words in the voice of a man, not young. Those in the chamber had heard Russian at one time or another, and they recognized it at once as Russian. It was subsequently established that the accent was of the south. Odessa. Which was where Professor Simeon Katlarsky had come from.

It was a moment or two before the startled translator collected her wits sufficiently for her to function.

> "—and the YAG laser, which I've described as a neodynium yitrium aggregate garnet beam, will serve both for electronic intelligence—the ELINT satellite system, as the United States calls it, and their FERRET satellite system which seeks out and gathers data. Our high-speed rockets with thrust of one hundred and seventy-five thousand kilograms requires a guidance system of the SX14 category. Countermeasures will involve cutting down our power systems while neutralizing enemy guidance systems. Our own computer banks will be calibrated to accept the outage so that their potential remains intact, and to be resumed when the threat is passed."

The chamber was silent except for the two voices and the slight mechanical sounds. The Assistant Secretary of Defense stood spellbound. His translator, caught up in her performance, had lost her nervousness and was keeping up with the words flowing from the subject's mouth.

"My God!" he thought. "It's legitimate." It was muttered half aloud, as if to himself, in surrendering any doubts and reservations he may have had.

Kondorf stood there, elated. He was in the clear at last. He had *delivered.* Any responsibility for this unscheduled demonstration was Gallagher's, not his. And as for Eli, he wouldn't even know what had happened. Tomorrow morning he could repeat the performance for the others with their little packages. If Eli became difficult again, even that wouldn't matter. The program would have been proved successful.

During this time, each preoccupied with his or her own tasks and thoughts, no one for several moments was aware of the tall gaunt figure standing on the threshold of the chamber with a forty-five-caliber automatic pistol, regulation issue, half raised in his hand. His eyes took in the entire scene. For a moment, there was a momentary flash of anger in those eyes. His gun hand started to raise. Then something in him seemed to take control. The gun lowered a bit.

The translator was the first to see the figure at the rear. Halfway through a difficult phrase to do with a spacecraft's ephemerous tracking, her words cut off. Gallagher's head turned, and following her stare he turned completely to face the cause of the interruption. Meanwhile, Professor Simeon Katlarsky continued speaking through the medium of a girl born on New York's Long Island.

By now, Kondorf and Jelke were aware of the intruder.

"Switch it off," Eli said to Jelke. The latter, however,

just stared. "Switch it *off,* I said." Jelke's hand went to the toggle and flicked it.

Connie's last words were . . . *"survivability ratio,"* but it was like the unwinding, dying gasp of an old Victrola, the words and the sound distorting before they expired completely. And with it, of course, began the rocking.

Eli, taking a cautious step into the room, positioned himself against the wall beside the entrance. "All of you —everyone—out," he said quietly.

They moved slowly. In passing Eli, they were certain he had gone off the deep end. Nothing about his looks discounted that. Kondorf, in passing, reached out a tentative hand. Smiling, he began, "Eli—" He got no further. The face he saw close to his suggested he stood very close to his own death.

When the last of them was gone, Eli raised a hand to the wall, opened a small receptacle and pushed a button. The monel metal doors to the chamber slid shut noiselessly.

Putting the weapon beneath his trouser belt, he drew a chair close to and in front of Connie. For a while he just looked at her, then he did a strange thing. It was an ordinary metal and leather chair he sat in, not a rocker. But in this seat, he began to rock his body, synchronizing his rhythm to hers.

"I've just about exhausted it," Phil Carlino said, explaining he couldn't find a single clue at the Institute. "Once or twice, I thought I had something but . . ." He shook his head hopelessly.

It was in the kitchen of the Nunn house. Rosarita, the housekeeper, no longer came, which was all right with Tessa. It didn't matter to her. That part of her life was done with. By the time Eli returned, she'd be gone anyhow.

Phil poured the wine, and they ate silently, each deep

in his own thoughts. She had served something heated over, which couldn't matter less to either of them.

"Incredible," she murmured.

"Whoever said government is inefficient? I suppose motivation is the name of the game."

"When will you leave? Go back?"

"Today. This afternoon," he told her, and it occurred to him, would anyone ever know . . . recognize him again? He surely wasn't the same person. "Take me somewhere before the airport?" he asked.

"Of course."

"Have you heard from him?"

"Not a word," she said.

The phone in the chamber rang several times, but Eli didn't seem to hear it. After a while it no longer rang. He wasn't even aware of the flame cutting through the metal doors, the smoke and the hissing, the torch outside, the agitated voice and the sound of metal against metal.

She rocked, and now he rocked. His concentration was like the oxyacetylene torch outside, as fierce as that, as penetrating. She gave him no sign. Nothing. There was no feedback. What he was feeling, thinking, he realized, was no more than the echo of himself. What he gave out came back to him—unchanged. And for him at this point —in this awful loneliness—he saw facing him the deep, dark grave of death.

Phil Carlino stood in the wooded glen behind the Sorrento Inn. It was "their place." Beyond, on the rise, almost hidden by the aspens and pines, was the wooden *torii* under which he and Connie had walked together. To this—"their place . . ."

The *koi* broke the pond's dark surface, ignoring the insects trapped there. A visitor had come, and a visitor meant handouts, as conditioning had taught them.

He stood now where they had first come into each other's arms. And with that brief letting-go, surrendering, a peace had come to him, a peace he'd come to associate with her. It came over him again like a thin veil. There were no words. This time not even his name. The sense was, it was all right . . . it was a safe place. But "their place," and neither would ever see it again . . .

Walking back, he turned at the *torii*. Looking back, he thought, Good-by.

They found them together. Dead. Eli lay at her feet, the single heavy-caliber bullet sufficient. She was declared dead by Dr. Jelke, who noticed at once that the valves of the support system had been closed off. It would have been instantaneous, he knew.

The others stood back, staring, unsure what they were seeing. A man and a woman dead, yes; but there was something more here. It was sensed by all of them. But whatever it was, they knew it was to be respected— forgiven.

Phil took his assigned seat after waving to Tessa. Settling down, someone else sat heavily in the neighboring seat. He looked about.

"Angie!"

" 'Lo, brother."

"What the hell? You were gone days ago—"

"Nah. I said why waste it."

"What?"

"I used to fly pigeons, 'member? Angie the Mumbler, they called me. Everybody. So I grew up to like—you know, to deal with animals. I deal with animals now. You didn't go to the San Diego Zoo."

"Zoo?"

"It's an unusual place," Angie said. He shook a newspaper open. On the same page was a short account of the body identified as a minor Mafia figure found in the vicinity of the home of the noted Elias Nunn. His eyes drifted to another item which meant nothing to him. Two unidentifiable bodies had been found in a blazing car wreck. Not even their sex could be determined.

"It was good to get away, Philly."

"What do you mean?"

"Makes you realize it's a general condition. Violence, I mean."

Some weeks later, Kondorf warmly greeted Dr. Richard Jelk as he entered his office.

"Come in, Dick, come in."

When the surgeon had been seated, the director of the Institute handed him a telegram.

"Washington. Read it."

Jelke did, then looked up, puzzled.

"I don't understand."

"Someone apparently forgot to turn off a computer."

The young neurosurgeon read the wire aloud. " 'A young twenty-four-year-old man in Honolulu struck on the head with his own surfboard.' "

"A simple fracture of the parietal bone. But there's some pressure and he's apparently in a coma. It shouldn't be too difficult, Dick. What do you think?"

Jelke stared at the director. He understood what was being asked of him, and he wasn't sure he was ready. He got up, went to the large window and stared out. Norville Kondorf kept silent. He knew the heavy bookkeeping that was going on. Even he was sometimes bothered by such judgments. But less and less so.

The real question was, was Richard Jelke ready to carry on?

He could wait for Jelke's answer. People like Kondorf had no alternative. There were born waiters. They served, and they did what they were told.

Well, what the hell, Kondorf thought. Somebody has got to see that the crazies don't take over the world. He smiled, feeling good, even superior to the weak geniuses he survived. In the end, by God, people like him were the strength, the best hope of the country. Damn right. Elias Nunn? All the Elias Nunns? To hell with him, and with them . . .

00747731 9 C. 2

Hammil
Limbo.